The Open University

Block 1

Who cares?

This publication forms part of an Open University course, K101 *An introduction to health and social care*. Details of this and other Open University courses can be obtained from the Student Registration and Enquiry Service, The Open University, PO Box 197, Milton Keynes MK7 6BJ, United Kingdom, tel. +44 (0)845 300 60 90, email general-enquiries@open.ac.uk

Alternatively, you may visit the Open University website at www.open.ac.uk where you can learn more about the wide range of courses and packs offered at all levels by The Open University.

To purchase a selection of Open University course materials, visit www.ouw.co.uk or contact Open University Worldwide, Walton Hall, Milton Keynes MK7 6AA, United Kingdom for a brochure, tel. +44 (0)1908 858793, fax +44 (0)1908 858787, email ouw-customer-services@open.ac.uk

The Open University
Walton Hall, Milton Keynes
MK7 6AA

First published 2008

Edited and designed by The Open University.

Typeset by SR Nova Pvt Ltd, Bangalore, India.

Printed in Malta by Gutenberg Press Limited

ISBN 978 0 7492 4642 6

1.1

Contents

Learning skills by Andrew Northedge

Introduction to Block 1

Welcome to your first block of study for K101 *An introduction to health and social care*. This block explores the question 'Who cares?' by considering the three main sources of care within our society:

- Unit 1 'Care: a family affair?' examines the immensely significant but often under-acknowledged caring that goes on, unpaid, as part of daily life within families and other households.

- Unit 2 'Illness, health and care' outlines the wide and constantly changing range of care provided through modern health services.

- Unit 3 'Social care in the community' explores the many forms of professional care work which are not directly part of health care and are generally brought together under the heading 'social care'.

As well as outlining the three broad types of care – family care, health care and social care – Block 1 also introduces you to the experience of studying. You will come to activities and 'learning skills' boxes which will show you how the different aspects of the course work. These will help you to get the most you can out of the course.

Rounding off the block is Unit 4 'Developing care relationships'. This is a shorter unit and is quite different, in that you will be working on skills rather than reading about a new topic. Finally, since studying always involves first taking in new ideas and then trying them out for yourself, there is an assignment at the end of the block which will help to bring together what you have learned and put it into your own words. Because you may not have done this kind of writing for a while, there is also a short practice assignment at the end of Unit 1.

We hope very much that you will find Block 1 relevant, challenging and stimulating.

Unit 1
Care: a family affair?

Prepared for the course team by Jan Walmsley

Contents

Introduction

This course is about care, about giving care and being at the receiving end of care. We all know about care from personal experience. As very small infants we would not have survived if someone hadn't, at the very least, fed us and kept us warm and fairly safe. As adults we also, most of us, want care. It's nice to be loved and welcomed, to have a meal prepared, to have the house cleaned. Much of this care happens in families. Many of our ideas about care come from ideas about how families should behave and what they should do. However, once childhood is out of the way, most people don't *need* care to stay alive, unless they are ill. Health care and social care come into the picture when people have exceptional needs for care – when they are unable to perform the tasks required for daily living without help from others.

The course takes you on a learning journey through health care and social care. It's a very complex field, and involves a huge number of people. According to the Department of Health (DH), in 2006 there were 15 million people in England with long-term health conditions, such as diabetes, stroke and high blood pressure (DH, 2006). Some 1.7 million people relied on social care services – mainly older people, but also younger adults with a range of disabling conditions. Well over 2 million people were employed in either health or social care. (The proportions are similar for Wales, Scotland and Northern Ireland.) However, these figures ignore what is undoubtedly the most significant source of care – the caring that goes on within families.

In the list below are the questions we will be trying to answer in Unit 1.

Core questions

- What is meant by care in the family context, and why does it matter?
- What is it like to experience care within families?
- Where is the boundary between carers and ordinary family members?
- What demands do care relationships place on people?

Are you taking the IVR?

If you are studying K101 as part of the Integrated Vocational Route (IVR), don't forget to check your VQ Candidate Handbook to see which Unit 1 activities contribute to your electronic portfolio.

1 Care in families: why it matters

This unit is about carers in families – people who support other family members who need help to manage the everyday tasks of living.

Using the right terms

In the past, family carers have often been called 'unpaid carers' or 'informal carers'. However, organisations representing carers argue that the terms 'unpaid' and 'informal' belittle what these carers do and that they should simply be called 'carers'. So this is now the generally accepted term. It also includes people who care for a friend or neighbour, although in this unit we concentrate on care within families. Meanwhile, people who care as a paid job tend to be called 'care workers', or 'care professionals'. A government website agrees:

> … the word 'carer' means someone who looks after a friend, relative or neighbour who needs support because of their sickness, age or disability.

> It does not mean a professional care-worker in a nursing home, for example – or someone employed by a disabled person.

> (Directgov, 2006)

1.1 What do family carers do?

Family members undertake a great many tasks that might loosely be called care, if we include such things as cooking, shopping and getting children ready for school. But, as you have seen, the term 'carer' is used specifically to mean looking after someone 'who needs support because of their sickness, age or disability'. And while *all* the caring that goes on within families plays a very important part in people's lives, the work of family 'carers' has a special significance, which we are going to explore in this unit.

The importance of family carers

Most 'care' stories in the media tend to be about hospitals, doctors, nurses and sometimes social workers, and about people with serious or life-threatening conditions. However, the fact is that most of the care of the millions of people who have long-term conditions, such as arthritis, diabetes and heart disease, or who are too old or disabled to manage without support, is provided within families. It was estimated that in 2006:

- There were 6 million people in the UK providing unpaid support to older, disabled or sick people.
- Their work saved £57 billion a year because the work carers do would have to be paid for if they did not do it (Carers UK, 2006).

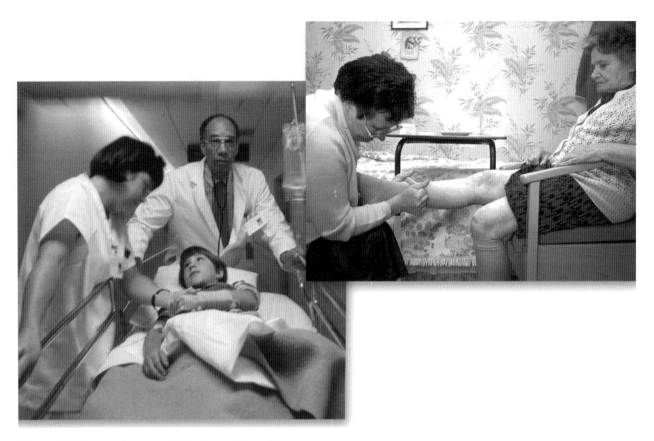

The public image of care and the domestic reality

The Carers (Recognition and Services) Act 1995 was the first government Act to recognise the work of family carers officially. The 1999 government publication *Caring about Carers: A National Strategy for Carers* puts it like this:

> Carers play a vital role – looking after those who are sick, disabled, vulnerable or frail. The Government believes that care should be something which people do with pride. We value the work that carers do. So we are giving new support to carers.

> (DH, 1999, p. 11)

Governments are interested in family carers because without them the cost of care for the millions of adults who need support to manage daily living would be unaffordable. A review of the care market in London in 2005, commissioned by the King's Fund, reckoned that:

> The massive impact that any reduction in informal care would have renders it impossible to effectively plan for the future.

> (Laing, 2005, p. 4)

The UK is one of the few countries in the world to have recognised that family carers are vitally important, and to have tried to find ways to enable them to 'carry on caring'.

What goes on within family care?

Who are the family carers? How can they be recognised? What are their lives like? How does someone, who is in everyday terms a mum, a son, a daughter-in-law, a partner or a spouse, become a carer, or a person officially deemed to be in need of care? These are the kinds of questions you will be exploring. To help you in this, you will be following an extended case study.

The story of Ann, Angus and their family

The case of Ann and Angus is based on research into carers carried out by Joyce Cavaye (2007). The names and some of the details have been changed and it has been dramatised to make the story come to life, but it is grounded in real people's experiences. It is not meant to be 'typical', but neither is it very unusual. It presents a situation which you might well recognise from experience with your own family, or families of people you know.

The people you will meet in the first part of the case study are:

- Angus McPhail, 79, a retired welder from the Glasgow shipyards, who has Parkinson's disease
- Ann Walker, 37, Angus' stepdaughter, who used to be a promotions assistant, but who has given up work because Angus has started to need more care
- Bob Walker, Ann's husband, a carpet fitter
- Zoe Walker, Ann and Bob's 12-year-old daughter
- Cheryl Ross, Ann's friend, who still works at the marketing company where she and Ann met.

The case of Ann and Angus raises important questions:

- Why do people become involved in caring for family members?
- What is the impact of caring on family relationships?
- Is there a need for outside support for families and, if so, how do people get that support?

First you need to acquaint yourself with the family, their circumstances and the challenges they face.

DVD

Activity 1   Getting to know Ann, Angus and family

Allow about 30 minutes

You first meet Ann and Angus by listening to them on the DVD.

You need access to a computer to do this.

If this is your first time using the DVD, you should read the section on using the K101 DVD in 'Getting Started Online'. Then put the DVD in your computer. When it starts up, read the 'Getting started' page carefully. Take a little time to look around the DVD and familiarise yourself with the way it works. (If you are confident with computers and DVDs, you can probably work a lot of it out as you go along.)

Then find Block 1, Unit 1, Activity 1, and follow the instructions on screen.

Comment

You have now met Ann and Angus and have some insight into the life they lead, the dynamics of life within their family and the strains experienced by all of them.

Activity 2   The background to Ann's caring role

Allow about 40 minutes

Now you need to know more about how Ann came to be caring for Angus and some of the complications of the circumstances under which the family is living.

Find Resource 1, 'Becoming and being a carer', by Joyce Cavaye in the Resources Book. Read as far as the heading 'Accessing services'.

Then write some notes in answer to these questions:

(a) When did Ann become a carer?

(b) Why did she feel she had 'no choice'?

(c) Did she regard herself as a carer?

Comment

Did you get the following points?

(a) Ann became a carer when her mother died and she took on responsibility for her father.

(b) She felt she had no choice but to do it because:

- She felt people expected it – it was a 'woman's job'.

- She, Bob and Zoe were already living in her parents' home when her mother died – she was on the spot.

- She had promised her mother that she would carry on looking after Angus.

(c) At this stage she 'did not recognise herself as a "carer". She saw herself first and foremost as a wife, mother and dutiful daughter'. Speaking to Cheryl, she said, 'I'm not a carer! It's just Dad, Bob and Zoe.' Then she said she was a 'full-time wife and mother. Like a lot of other women who don't make a deal out of it'.

Ann's story shows how family members may find themselves with caring responsibilities and feeling that they don't have much choice about it. Like Ann, they may not think of themselves as carers, yet they may find themselves doing things they have never had to do before, and coming under unanticipated stresses which alter relationships within the family. Caring responsibilities can creep up on people, so that they are not fully aware of the extent of what they have taken on, and the demands it places on them and other family members.

Learning skills: Working with the DVD

In Activity 1, you had your first experience of using the DVD. Or did you? Were you able to get access to a computer? Do you have your own computer, or do you have to go somewhere to use one? If you don't have easy access to a computer, what is your strategy going to be when you come to an activity which uses the DVD?

K101 uses a computer for listening to and viewing audio and video material because this allows for exercises that are much more 'interactive'. We can set up easy-to-follow activities around the audio and video recordings and you can type notes directly into prepared note sheets. It is actually a DVD-ROM rather than a DVD, which means that you cannot see the learning exercises if you put it in an ordinary DVD player. So you will need access to a computer.

- If you have easy access to a computer then all should be straightforward. Just follow the instructions as you come to them.

- If, on the other hand, you have to make special arrangements, such as borrowing a computer or going somewhere to use one, then we suggest that you work on all the DVD activities for a unit just before you start reading it. Just put the DVD in the computer, find the block and unit you are about to study, and work your way through the activities. Print off your notes as you go and then you will have them ready when you come to the relevant activity.

Either way, you will find that the DVD activities bring the course to life. With all the direct insight into caring situations that the DVD provides, everything you learn about will make a lot more sense.

The DVD plays a very important part in K101 and you will need to make full use of it. If you didn't manage to get to a computer to work on Activity 1, you should try to complete it as soon as you can in order to get the most you can from the rest of Unit 1.

1.2 Who counts as a carer?

In Activity 1, we heard that Ann does not see herself as a carer. But then Cavaye's article talks about her becoming a carer. So is she a carer, or not? She certainly qualifies as 'someone who looks after a friend, relative or neighbour who needs support because of their sickness, age or disability' – to quote the government website's definition of a carer. But *Ann* thinks that the things she does are just what a daughter would be expected to do. So how might we decide whether to consider her as a carer?

DVD

Activity 3   What does Ann do for Angus?

Allow about 20 minutes

It's time to listen to Ann and Angus again in order to tease out the extent and nature of the caring tasks Ann undertakes.

Go to the DVD and find Block 1, Unit 1, Activity 3.

Comment

You have seen that Ann does a lot with Angus that a daughter would not usually do with her father, including things that are normally private and personal. And in general, she spends a lot more time focused on his needs than you would expect for an adult family member.

Does this make Ann a carer? In fact, she does most of the tasks that two researchers (Parker and Lawton, 1994) identified as being what carers do:

- She performs personal services, such as washing and toileting.
- She does physical labour – helping Angus up the stairs, and in and out of bed.
- She gives him his medicine.
- She keeps him company.

All this is well beyond the normal role of a daughter. Yet coming to think of yourself as a carer rather than a daughter, or a homemaker, is a big step. It changes the way you think about yourself – in this case, from being an affectionate daughter to being someone whose identity lies in caring for another. Ann does it because she loves Angus. Moreover, she promised her mother on her death bed that she would look after him. She gave up work willingly because it was 'the right thing to do'. But recognising herself as a carer would mean facing up to the fact that Angus is not going to get better, and that her new situation is a permanent one, likely to become more stressful as his illness progresses. Moreover, if she accepts Cheryl's suggestion that she needs help, she may feel as if she is failing when she ought to be able to cope.

Because caring is often hidden within families, as in Ann's case, carers are not always known about. At what point someone stops being 'just a family member' and becomes identifiable as a 'carer' is not easy to decide. And this is more difficult when the person who needs care has a condition that fluctuates, being worse at some times than at others. This is true of Angus. On 'good days' he's pretty capable, but on bad days he needs constant care and attention. So Ann is more of a carer on some days than she is on others.

Why does it matter?

Why are we spending a lot of time trying to decide whether Ann is a carer? Does it matter?

It would matter to a number of people:

- to Ann if she wanted to apply for financial or practical support
- to budget holders who need to be able to plan carer support services
- to organisations (such as Carers UK) which campaign for the needs of carers, and want to know how many people they represent
- to employers who are obliged to take account of employees' caring responsibilities (Directgov, 2007).

It would also matter greatly if, for any reason, Ann was unable to continue and other arrangements were needed for Angus at short notice.

Is Ann officially a carer?

If Ann fulfils the definition of a carer from the government website quoted at the start of Section 1 – as 'someone who looks after a … relative … who needs support because of their sickness, age or disability', does that make her 'officially' a carer? Well, that definition is a very broad one. Ann does a lot for her father, but many people do less, and would still meet the definition.

However, if Ann were to apply for financial help she would need to meet a more rigorous definition. To qualify for a Carer's Allowance, she would be required meet the following conditions. She would need to:

- be caring for someone for at least thirty-five hours a week

- be over sixteen, and not a student

- be caring for someone formally recognised as 'disabled' (e.g. someone who qualifies for the Disability Living Allowance care component – higher or middle rate) or someone over sixty-five (to qualify for Attendance Allowance)

- not earn more than £95 per week.

(The figures given here were correct as at February 2008. If you would like to check for more up-to-date figures, consult the carers' pages on www.directgov.uk.)

If these requirements are taken as a definition of what it is to be a carer, then it is more difficult to decide whether Ann officially qualifies as a carer. Caring for Angus is more or less a full-time job, although some of the things she does, such as cooking meals, are done for the whole family, not just for Angus. And, as we have noted, his condition changes – sometimes he needs a lot more of her time and energy than at other times. Also, Angus would need to accept to some degree that he *needs* care, as it is he, not Ann, who must apply for Attendance Allowance.

What are the advantages of being recognised as a carer?

Would it help Ann if she were recognised as a carer? If she qualified for a Carer's Allowance she would get £45.70 per week (as of July 2007; you can check the carers' pages on www.directgov.uk for any update to this). Unlike normal wages, it does not increase the more you do, but it is at least something. Also, Ann might get practical help and support. Angus might receive care from paid workers, and Ann might get support directly targeted at her needs. The Carers Equal Opportunities Act 2004, which came into force in England and Wales in 2005, put carers in England and Wales on a par with those in Scotland. It gives carers the right to an assessment of their needs, with regard not just to their caring role, but also to their needs for leisure, training and work. In addition, the Act places a duty on local authorities to let carers know about the support they are entitled to. Carers may also be entitled to Home Responsibility Protection, so that their pensions are protected while they are not in employment (The Pension Service, 2007).

However, as you have seen, it is quite a big step to say 'I'm a carer'. It is also a big step to say 'I am cared for' – and one that is often resisted. As the story unfolds, you will hear just what Angus thinks about being identified as someone who needs care from outside the family.

At first sight, the government definition of a carer seems to be straightforward. But if you are looking for support, it becomes much stricter.

Complicating factors

Deciding whether someone is a carer is often difficult because the circumstances can be so complicated and uncertain. We now look at four factors which complicate the picture. The first is to do with how much time the person spends on caring activities and how frequent these are.

Duration and frequency

In order to decide whether someone is officially a carer, the amount of caring they do needs to be counted in some way. The Government has decided that caring for more than thirty-five hours a week qualifies a person for the Carer's Allowance. Ann reckoned that she did care for Angus for thirty-five hours.

Washing and toileting	2 hours a day, 7 days a week = 14 hours
Helping Angus up and down the stairs, in and out of bed	1.5 hours a day, 7 days a week = 10.5 hours
Giving Angus his medicine and applying cream to his piles	1.5 hours a day, 7 days a week = 10.5 hours
Total	35 hours

Ann also keeps Angus company, makes him cups of tea, fetches his water, switches on the television – tasks which are difficult to quantify in hours.

But, as we have noted, Angus' condition is sometimes worse than at other times, and Ann acknowledged that she did less caring some weeks than others. Also, she pointed out to Joyce Cavaye that some of the work she does for Angus would have to be done anyway, for herself and her family. So counting exactly how much time any carer spends is bound to be an inexact science.

Totting up the hours and minutes spent on care

Labelling and identity

The term 'carer' is a label. And to get support you need to accept this label. But labelling yourself as a carer requires a shift from seeing yourself as a daughter or a mum. On the DVD, when Ann rings the 'social', the duty social worker asks: 'Are you the carer?'. Her answer is 'Not exactly – well I suppose so, I look after him'. Suddenly, from doing what she is doing out of love, she is being seen by the world of officials as a 'carer'. The price of getting help is to say 'yes, I am the carer'. And Ann is initially reluctant to change her identity in this way.

If it is difficult for Ann, it seems equally difficult for Angus to learn to regard himself as a 'cared for person'. It is understandable that he wants to retain a sense of himself as a family member and homeowner, rather than as someone who is so seriously ill that his daughter needs to be his carer. In Section 2, you will consider in more depth how this feels.

Interdependence

Caring is not always simple and one way. People in families may give support to each other, so that it becomes difficult to say who is carer and who is cared for. What if Angus reciprocated Ann's care in some way – say, by looking after Zoe or helping her with her homework?

An older person caring for a younger one

Networks

There are a number of people involved in caring for Angus. Ann may do the lion's share, but Bob and Zoe can contribute too, at least by keeping him company, but perhaps also by getting him things. And Bob helped when Angus was struggling with the stairs. Michael Fine, an expert on care, argues that there is a cost in defining 'carer' too closely as it 'serves to focus attention on one person regarded as the caregiver … Others who provide care are thereby excluded including neighbours, friends, teachers, volunteers, also the parents and step parents of children who are not defined as disabled, similarly grandparents' (Fine, 2007, p. 30). However, if Bob or Zoe helped quite a lot, might that count against Ann being formally recognised as a carer? And what of Cheryl? She does not care directly for Angus, but in her support for Ann she too plays an important part. She was the one who pressed for seeking support.

To explore further these complications of deciding whether someone is a carer, try the next activity.

Activity 4 Spot the carer?

Allow about 10 minutes

Read the two paragraphs below, sent in by people who tested this course in its draft stage, and then answer the following question.

In the light of what you know about who is defined as a carer, would you count Evelyn and Sean as carers? Give your reasons.

Evelyn:

> I think I'm an informal carer now. I'm a single parent. My daughter Marie is three, and I struggle with trying to earn a living and bringing her up better than my mum brought me up. I work part time because life on benefits was just grim, I was poor and I was lonely. I'm still poor, I'm not as lonely though. Anyway, I think I should qualify for Carer's Allowance. I do at least a 35-hour week with Marie. I earn less than £82 a week. The only difference is Marie is not on a Disability Allowance. Otherwise I'm just as needy as any other carer.

Sean:

> When I was at school I lived with my dad and my younger brother – my mum had disappeared and I still don't know where she went. But I think I know why – dad was an alcoholic and my brother Conor has Down's syndrome. So I was left doing quite a lot at home. I used to get my brother up for school, and see him on the bus. After I'd finished school I had to rush home to make sure I was there to meet him when the bus dropped him home – luckily he was bussed quite a long way so I could get there first. I'd get him his tea – and me. At weekends I'd go into town on the bus to get the shopping in. I didn't actually do much for my dad, but I knew if I wasn't there the household would grind to a halt. Reading this made me think I probably was a carer – except it all started when I was under sixteen. I never got any help because no one knew about us, and no one ever asked.

Comment

Evelyn does not fit the Government's definition of a carer. She is doing what 'mums' do – looking after her 3-year-old daughter. If all mothers of young children were to be called 'carers', it would open up all kinds of questions, such as whether all women should be paid for their mothering responsibilities.

Sean might have been eligible for help if anyone had known about his situation. He would be in another category: a 'young carer'.

There are many people who do a great deal of caring, but who do not easily fit the official definition of a carer discussed so far.

1.3 Getting to grips with family care

Family care may seem a rather ordinary and unremarkable activity. Certainly it seldom hits the headlines. However, we have seen that there is far more to family care than there may seem.

The importance of care in families

Care in families is important not just to the estimated 6 million carers and the people they care for, but, as we saw in Section 1.1, also to the Government, which recognises that if family carers were not available, enormous costs would be incurred in paying workers to do the work family carers do.

Challenges of defining what carers do

Care may be defined broadly in a way which encompasses most situations where members of families, or friends, contribute to the care of someone who needs assistance with daily living. However, official definitions that define eligibility for financial and practical support are stricter. Definitions of the work of carers are important because they enable helping agencies to target their resources, but they also exclude people who fall below the threshold.

Challenges of identifying carers

This section has also introduced some of the challenges of identifying carers. Care relationships can be hidden in families for a long time. People who care, and people who are cared for, may resist being labelled in this way. And as we have seen, measuring how much care someone gives is never going to be precise.

Key points

- Carers are family members who provide care for another person who is sick or unable to manage daily life unaided.
- Governments are interested in family care because, without family carers, providing care would be prohibitively expensive.
- It is important to identify carers so that help, and in some cases financial support, can be provided.
- However, it can be difficult to identify carers because:
    - Much of what happens in families is private.
    - Many people resist being labelled as a carer or a cared for person.
    - It can be hard to measure how much caring someone does.
    - Some caring is reciprocal: there is give and take.
    - More than one person may be involved in caring.

Learning skills: Working with the K101 'boxes'

As you work through K101 you will come to boxes of various kinds. These provide a kind of parallel conversation about various things that are part of the course, although not directly within the mainstream of the subject matter you are learning about. The boxes are written so that you can read them on their own, without necessarily knowing what comes before and after. You can also read straight past them if you are keen to follow the discussion in the main text. In other words, they are strategically placed at points where they are relevant, but you can make your own choices about when to read them. However, you shouldn't ignore them because they provide important ideas and information.

You have already come across a case study box and now a second learning skills box. The case study boxes are self-explanatory, but it is worth thinking about how to make best use of the learning skills boxes.

Learning skills boxes

This box you are reading is a learning skills box (you met one of these after Activity 2). These boxes form part of the learning skills strand that runs throughout K101. If you have not studied for a while, or not at this level, then this aspect of the course will be as important to you as the care topics you learn about. Most people find studying with the OU an excellent way to learn:

> For the third year running The Open University tops the National Student Survey for overall satisfaction.

(ePolitix.com, 2007)

However, you need to be able to plan sensibly, find your way past obstacles and keep your spirits up when things aren't going as well as you had hoped. To help you keep on top of your studies, the learning skills boxes:

- offer ideas and tips for tasks you are currently working on
- suggest activities to help you experiment with different ways of learning
- encourage you to think back over the learning you have just been doing, in order to draw out general lessons for your future studies
- point you towards sections of *The Good Study Guide* which are relevant to the issues you are exploring.

If you follow these guidelines, by the end of the course you will have read most of *The Good Study Guide*. But don't wait to be directed – just dip into the book whenever you want ideas or advice. It's designed to be read that way. Use the index at the back to find what you are looking for. The combination of the learning skills boxes and *The Good Study Guide* will give you a thorough introduction to all the learning skills you need for this and future courses.

Can you afford to be distracted?

Sometimes you may feel that stopping to read a learning skills box will disrupt the flow of your studies. (Perhaps you feel that right now.) However, your skills will develop better if you work on them while you are in the middle of the learning process. In the long run it will save you time. And studying will be much more satisfying if you have a clear idea of what you are doing and a range of well-developed skills to draw on.

2 Experiencing family care

This section continues with the story of Ann and her family, but now the focus is on the experience of being in long-term care relationships.

2.1 What is it like to care?

Resources

Activity 5   What is it like being a carer?

Allow about 25 minutes

Reread Resource 1, from the section heading 'Going it alone' to the heading 'Accessing services'. Using the information and what you recall from the DVD, jot down some words which describe what caring is like for Ann, and next to each word or phrase, write down examples to illustrate it.

Comment

Here is my list, which is probably not exactly the same as yours.

- **Hard work**. Ann has to lift Angus onto the toilet and manoeuvre him up the stairs.
- **Demanding skill**. Ann has learned how to manage Angus' care.
- **Restricting**. Ann has given up her career.
- **Stressful**. Angus is in pain; Ann has lots of competing demands on her time.
- **Isolated**. Ann spends a lot of time alone with Angus, and does not get out much.
- **Emotionally demanding**. Angus relies on Ann to be kind, patient and cheerful. Bob and Zoe also want more attention and affection than she offers. All of them take their frustrations out on her at times.
- **Guilt provoking**. Ann feels guilty about not caring well enough for Angus and for shouting at him, and about not giving sufficient attention and time to Bob and Zoe.
- **Trapped by a sense of duty**. Ann feels it is her duty to care for Angus, especially after the promise she made to her mother.
- **Obligation**. Ann, Bob and Zoe are living in Angus' house, and he does not let them forget that.
- **Frightening**. Ann and Angus fall on the landing and might fall down the stairs.
- **Rewarding**. They share a few tender moments; she knows he appreciates the help she gives him.

The list includes quite a mixture of experiences. Ann says she would not do anything else, but her decision to care for Angus has consequences, not just for her, but for her family too. She is not available to give them attention. Her income has gone, and nothing has replaced it. She can be bad tempered. Bob is worried about her well-being – and his own. Zoe's concerns are neglected.

Caring is about love
and it is about work

Ann's experiences of being a carer are not uncommon. Many studies have shown that carers find it hard work; it impacts on their careers and social life, and caring is emotionally intense and often very lonely (Carers UK, 2003, 2005). Ann is relatively well off in comparison with many carers:

- She loves Angus.

- She is relatively young and in good health.

- She has her Bob and Zoe – even though not everything is harmonious, she is not alone all the time with Angus, in the way many carers are alone with the person they care for.

- She has a friend, Cheryl, to go out with.

- Although the family is not well off, she does not seem to be overwhelmed by worries about money.

The images of carers presented in research studies and the media often emphasise the burden of caring. Organisations representing carers, such as Carers UK, have a case to make that carers need a better deal, more support and recognition. But it is easy to overstate the negatives. Caring is about love and it is about work. It is sometimes described as both love and labour. In some family care relationships the labour is paramount. In others, it is more mixed. Caring can be two-way, with the person being cared for giving as well as receiving. It is important to remember that for many people, caring for someone they love brings immense rewards.

2.2 What affects care relationships?

If the experience of care varies from person to person, how can this be explained? Is it just that everyone is different?

To answer this, we turn to some of the extensive research which has been produced on caring in families. Three key messages from this research are that caring relationships are influenced by:

- the quality of the relationship, particularly before caring commenced (Lewis and Meredith, 1988; Finch and Mason, 1992; Forbat, 2005)

- how much choice people have in becoming the carer, and in how they manage the caring (Lewis and Meredith, 1988; Forbat, 2005)

- the amount and nature of external support received (Lewis and Meredith, 1988; Carers UK, 2003, 2005).

These ideas will be explored in relation to the case study.

Quality of relationship

Jane Lewis and Barbara Meredith (1988), in a study of daughters caring for their mothers, single out the previous relationship between mother and daughter as one of the most important determinants of the daughters' attitudes to caring for their mothers. Liz Forbat (2005), who interviewed six pairs of people involved in family care relationships, also argues that caring roles and relationships need to be considered with regard to the past history of the relationship. People become carer and cared for in the context of an existing relationship, so some of the strengths and weaknesses of those relationships are played out in the care relationship. In short, it is easier to care for someone you like and get along with.

Does this shed light on the situation in the case study?

Angus had always been a rather domineering figure. Ann had at times been rebellious and argumentative when younger, but had learned to curb her tongue because it upset her mother when she and Angus argued. Now it is quite awkward to manage the relationship. Much of the time, Angus does not appear to recognise that Ann may have needs of her own, and that Bob and Zoe also need her. He tries to order her about, becoming quite impatient when his demands are not met immediately. She does not want to draw too much attention to his loss of power, nor does she want to become his servant, so it's hard for her to respond. His swings between trying to lay down the law and becoming almost childlike, clinging to her for support, wrenching Ann's emotions. I imagine that she wrestles with a mixture of pity, revulsion and affection.

I am inclined to the view that if Angus were more patient, and had more insight into Ann's situation, the caring could have been considerably less difficult to manage.

Choice

Researchers argue that if people make a positive choice to care then it is likely to be a more enjoyable experience. However, this is not straightforward either. Ann said to Joyce Cavaye that she had no choice. At this stage, she really did not know that she could make any choices about caring for Angus, other than putting him into a care home. It is a common criticism that people are frequently not aware of the range of alternatives to caring for relatives themselves. In a study of carers' experience of discharge from hospital, entitled *You Can Take Him Home Now* (Carers National Association, 2001), 70% of those surveyed said they had not been offered any choice but to carry on caring – they were not told about services such as home care and day centres.

Whether someone chooses to care is also complicated by questions of duty and expectations. Ann illustrates this well. She promised her mother she would care for Angus, and she feels bound by the promise. She also reckons she owes Angus something, saying to Cheryl, 'Now it's payback time'. The idea that parents earn a right to be cared for because they invested so much in bringing up their children is held strongly in many families (Finch, 1989) and across different cultures (Jones and Rupp, 2000).

Choice can also be about how you manage your life as a carer. Ann did not think she had any choice about giving up her job as Angus' situation deteriorated. A survey by Carers UK, entitled *Missed Opportunities* and published in 2003, found that many carers would have liked to carry on with their jobs, but that they could not get the type of support needed to make that possible.

Financial considerations also play a part in whether people choose to care. If Ann and Bob had been able to afford their own home earlier, before Ann's mother died, they would not have been as available to care for Angus. As it was, Angus took his opportunities to remind them that he owned the house.

It is estimated that one-third of carers live in poverty. Most carers give up their jobs. Extra costs, such as adapting the home, changing the car to accommodate a wheelchair, extra heating, all help to explain why one-third of carers qualify for Income Support. Poverty means lack of choice. People with enough money can make arrangements for caring which allow them to carry on with their lives. But many people do not have this choice. Financial necessity is often a factor in becoming a carer, and the need to give up or reduce employment means that opportunities to change your mind are rare.

So, to say that someone has made a choice to care is more complicated than it seems at first sight. To make a choice to care you need to know that there are acceptable alternatives; you need to feel entitled to resist the strong social pressures that you ought to take it on; and you need to be able to afford the costs of making changes. Beware choice!

Support

The amount of support carers get makes a big difference to their ability to cope with caring. It is useful to divide support into two categories:

- informal support, from families and friends
- formal support, from outside agencies.

Informal support is certainly a mixed bag as far as Ann is concerned. She does not get much direct help from anyone in caring for Angus. Bob and Zoe do not appear to do much for Angus, and although Bob shows he cares for Ann by cooking an anniversary meal, the gesture backfires because of Angus. Zoe, with her moods and difficulties at school, is another demand on Ann, rather than being a support to her. But she does have Cheryl, and the relationship seems to be important, not only because she can pour her heart out to Cheryl, but also because she gets an independent source of advice, telling her she does have choices if she decides to exercise them.

Ann does not get any formal support from outside agencies at this stage in the story. She rejected Cheryl's idea that she needed it. But a series of crises changed all that. In Unit 3, you will be considering how Ann got proper support from external agencies, and the difference it made.

2.3 Wife, mother, daughter, carer

Ann may be free of some of the challenges faced by other carers, such as isolation, serious financial worries or caring for someone whom she actively dislikes (although she had rows with Angus when she was a young woman). But she is faced with other challenges, which arise from trying to combine the roles of wife and mother with caring for Angus.

DVD

Activity 6   Torn between roles

Allow about 20 minutes

As well as being a carer, Ann has three important roles in the family – mother, wife and daughter. To think about how well she is able to play all these roles, you return now to the DVD to listen to the next instalment of the drama.

Go to the DVD and find Block 1, Unit 1, Activity 6.

Comment

Ann is pulled in several different directions at once. It seems that she puts her roles as carer and daughter first and second, and her roles as mother and wife tend to come third and fourth.

- **Mother**. Zoe has needs as well, but Ann appears to have limited attention to spare for considering whether Zoe is having problems at school, so she is completely taken aback when the teacher phones about her.
- **Wife**. Bob also feels neglected. It comes to a head when Bob and Ann's evening together is spoilt by Angus' demands and by Ann's decision to respond to them rather than prioritise the celebration with her husband.
- **Daughter**. Ann seems to have difficulty finding the right balance in being a calm, attentive carer while resisting being dominated as a daughter by her father.

You may think this is hard on Ann. Bob, after all, does not notice Zoe's needs either. He sees Angus as Ann's job. He does little to help, insisting on his football taking priority over Ann's evening out with Cheryl. His acerbic relationship with Angus adds to the tension in the household. He appears to take the view that caring – for him, for Zoe, and, if necessary, for Angus – is a woman's role.

Caring: a woman's role?

Ann has taken what is traditionally seen as a woman's role. She says herself 'that's a woman's job'. Although many men are carers, they care mostly for their wives or partners, and take on that task later in life, so rarely have to combine caring for an adult with care of children (Evandrou, 1990).

Learning skills: Studying actively

You have come across several 'activities' now. How are you approaching them? Do you stop to think and make notes? Do you spend the amount of time suggested? Or are you tempted to skip straight to the discussions following the activities?

As an independent adult student, paying your own way, you are free to approach all elements of K101 as you think best. Indeed, to learn well you need to achieve a sense of control over your own patterns of study. You have to be able to think strategically and make your own choices about how much time to give to different elements of the course. But so that you can allocate your time wisely, we should explain the idea behind the activities.

The point of studying is to learn new ideas. That takes more than just reading. It requires you to think for yourself as you go along. But in your drive to get to the end of each week's study, it is easy to let the words of the course simply 'wash over you', so the activities are put there to engage your thoughts – to help you make connections between your existing knowledge and experience and what you are reading about in the course.

To make proper use of the activities you need to jot down your own thoughts. Writing turns study from a passive process of 'soaking up' to an active process of 'making sense'. The activities are very varied and some are quite challenging. But even if you can't get fully to grips with some, just get *something* jotted down before looking at the comment following the activity. Then you can compare your own thoughts with the author's. Often, authors' notes will look quite different from yours. That doesn't matter. The effort of concentration in jotting down your own notes, and the stimulus to your thinking when you compare them with ours, will help to lodge new ideas in your head.

Your notes from activities can be a very useful resource when you are writing assignments or revising for the exam. It's a good idea to keep them all together in a folder. The activities are numbered, which should help you to keep your folder in order.

We give a rough time guide for each activity. It's up to you whether you spend more or less time, but be wary of spending a lot longer, or you may get thrown off schedule with your studies.

2.4 The other side of the relationship: what is it like to be cared for?

In focusing on carers, it is easy to overlook the person on the other side of the relationship. How does it feel to be on the receiving end? People who are cared for have certainly received less attention than carers from governments. Forbat (2005) notes that government pronouncements – like the statement in the Government's *National Strategy for Carers* that 'Carers play a vital role, looking after those who are sick, disabled, vulnerable or frail' (DH, 2000, p. 11) – make heroes of carers, but leave the people who receive care without an active part to play. They are just 'sick, disabled, vulnerable or frail'.

And, although there are many groups campaigning on behalf of disabled people or people with long-term health conditions – groups like the Parkinson's Disease Society (see below) – there is no 'Cared for UK' to speak up for all the people on the receiving end of care, to collect the statistics, or to make the case for change and improved services. But these people are people, too, with strong feelings about their situation, and there is plenty of evidence within the case study about how Angus feels.

What we do

The Parkinson's Disease Society was established in 1969.

We fund research that is focused on transforming lives. We have invested more than £35m since the charity was founded. This research has led to advances in the search for the cause of Parkinson's, improved medical and surgical treatments, better therapies and equipment, and towards finding a cure.

From the Parkinson's Disease Society website

Parkinson's disease

Angus has Parkinson's disease. This is a condition which affects about one in 500 people in the UK. It is the result of a loss of nerve cells in a part of the brain which coordinates movement. It affects mainly, but not exclusively, older people. Its cause is unknown.

Parkinson's affects people in different ways, but there are three symptoms common to most people with the condition:

1 tremor: uncontrollable shaking

2 muscular stiffness: making it difficult to do everyday tasks

3 slowness of movement.

It can also affect sleep, balance and mood, leading to depression, and it often leads to loss of confidence. It is a fluctuating condition: some days are worse than others.

The Parkinson's Disease Society seeks to represent people with Parkinson's disease, and their carers.

(Source: adapted from Parkinson's Disease Society, 2005)

DVD

Activity 7   Being cared for

Allow about 25 minutes

The purpose of this activity is to help you get inside Angus' experience.

Go to the DVD and find Block 1, Unit 1, Activity 7.

Comment

Angus seems to have quite a number of fears, but it is more difficult to identify his hopes.

We can summarise Angus' experiences of being dependent on Ann's care as largely negative, in spite of all her efforts and despite the fact that he is fond of her.

Loss of power and control

Parkinson's disease sometimes deprives Angus of control over the most basic functions of daily life. He has to depend on someone else for his very existence.

This is what a young woman, Amelia, who suddenly became dependent on other people's care at the age of eighteen, had to say about what it feels like to be made a dependant in this way:

> I think when I first regained consciousness after my injury I was too ill to realise that everything was being done for me. However a bit later I was living with my mum in the community and became very miserable because I realised how limited my existence was and how much I had to depend on others. Losing my independence after the injury was the hardest part of the whole ordeal. I went from a carefree 18 year old woman to a baby. My timetable was filled on my behalf, I was told when

I had to be where and how to get there. I was scared to try to do things on my own so I always relied on a companion.

(Personal communication)

Amelia's account indicates some of the feelings that are common to people who find themselves suddenly in a position of dependence on others.

Feeling a burden

Angus does not admit to feeling a burden directly, but some things he says hint at it, with phrases like 'don't mind me, I'm not long for this world'. His insistence that they are living in his house can possibly be understood as a reminder that he contributes something to the household, to counteract his sense of being a burden.

Fear

It is quite frightening to be in Angus' position. As you heard, he almost fell down the stairs. He does not know how the Parkinson's will affect him from one day to the next. Even a loving carer like Ann can be rough sometimes – at one point in the drama Angus complained that she was hurting him when she washed him too roughly.

Being helpless can mean being in danger. Families are not always safe havens. For her book *Independent Lives* (1993), researcher Jenny Morris interviewed people who were cared for. Vicky was one, living with her partner, Lorraine. She described an incident:

> One night she was putting me to bed. When I lie on my back, my arms are up by my ears, they don't lie flat at my side and … I have to have two pillows under my legs to be comfortable and while she was doing this she took up the pillow and held it over my face … You know when you're past that stage of holding your breath … you know, when you would take a gasp of breath, it was past that stage. And when she took it off, I tried not to gasp … and there I was, she lifted it slightly and then she did it again hard. And then she took it off and carried on quite normally putting me to bed …

(Quoted in Morris, 1993, p. 84)

As you can well imagine, many incidents of this kind go unreported. But older people who rely on families are particularly vulnerable. Drawing on the best evidence they could find in 2004, the House of Commons Health Committee reckoned that there were about half a million cases of abuse of older people each year, of which most took place in their own homes, at the hands of family members or paid carers (House of Commons Health Committee, 2004).

Isolation

Angus does not see many people. He can't get out by himself. For some people on the receiving end of care, their condition is such that they cannot sustain a social life without help. Angus relies on Ann for every little thing, and he was left out of the anniversary meal. Outings for Angus simply are not on the agenda, and he doesn't appear to have any friends of his own.

Lack of choice

This is similar to the carers' situation. People who are cared for may want to exercise choice, but may well lack the opportunity. Angus wanted to wash himself, but Ann insisted on doing it for him – it was quicker. Angus did try to exercise some choice, over the TV remote control, but in fact, as the anniversary scene shows, he wasn't in any position to insist.

Angus had no opportunities to make choices about the type of assistance he wanted. He did not want anyone other than Ann to look after him. In the end, he had no choice but to agree when Ann made up her mind to ask for help. Ann sought help from 'the social' without telling him that she was doing so. Angus was then faced with having the most intimate tasks, which Ann had done for him up until then, being performed by a stranger, and he had no choice in the matter.

Like Ann, Angus did not have information about support that might be available to him, even of a basic kind, such as a stairlift or grab rails.

It all sounds rather bleak, and for some people, including Angus at this stage of the drama, it probably is. Not only does he have a life-limiting condition – Parkinson's disease – he has lost his wife and he sees his life closing up and the world carrying on without him. No wonder he gets angry.

Being cared for does not always have to be so bleak. Amelia, the young woman quoted above, gives an illustration of the way in which family attitudes and expectations can open the way for building confidence:

> I am grateful to my family for being determined in allowing me to make small steps on my own. I acknowledge that the instinct is to wrap someone in cotton wool after a trauma like the one I had but my family encouraged me to take the bus or call my friends and other small accomplishments. At the time it was incredibly hard but I can see now that this (seemingly) hardlined approach prevented me from becoming even more infantile and meant that my self esteem was not eroded even more than it was already.

> In retrospect I feel strongly that if a person is suddenly in the position where they have to depend on others, the most helpful thing that can be done for them is to empower them to take some control of their own life.

> (Personal communication)

At this stage of the story, even though he makes some attempts to exercise power, maximising Angus' ability to take some control over his life is not on Ann's agenda. It is as much as she can do to keep going.

Amelia's story indicates that it does not have to be like this. As the drama unfolds, you will consider how Angus might be supported to take back some control over his life.

Learning skills: Learning from video and audio recordings

You have now visited the Ann and Angus audio drama four times. Did you feel you were able to draw out different things on each visit? Recorded material is usually a rich resource, with many different strands of meaning running through it. When we talk or write about care we can only pursue one main line of discussion at a time, whereas real life is immensely complicated and open to lots of different interpretations. That is why the DVD is such an important resource. It puts you directly in touch with the care world and allows you to think your own thoughts, coming at things from various different angles as you reflect on what you have heard and seen. Often you may not be quite sure what you have learned. But once the material is sitting in your head, you will make connections with it as you work on other parts of the course. It's a different kind of learning – broad and hazy and often difficult to pin down – but it is deep learning and just as important as the 'book learning' you will be doing.

Sometimes you have to listen through or view a whole recording to get the broad picture, before you can get down to detailed thinking about what points you can draw out. With the Ann and Angus drama, there is a host of things you could focus on. What is the impact of Ann's carer role on Zoe's upbringing? What is happening to Ann and Bob's relationship and what priority should it have compared with Ann's carer role? Is Ann approaching her caring tasks in appropriate ways? Does she have the right skills? You have made notes on all these different issues and still there is one more activity. Later you may want to go back to listen again, perhaps when you are writing an essay, or just to follow up an idea you've had. It's up to you. You have a resource here that is available to use when you want to.

2.5 Asking for help

In part four of the case study you heard that Ann had finally decided to ask 'the social' for help with looking after Angus. Cavaye found in her research with carers that it was usually a crisis of some sort that prompted people to recognise that they simply weren't coping (Cavaye, 2007).

DVD

Activity 8   What made Ann ask for help?

Allow about 20 minutes

Several factors combined to push Ann into action. To explore these, go to the DVD and find Block 1, Unit 1, Activity 8.

Comment

The most obvious trigger was, as Cavaye's research suggests, a crisis. The combination of the outburst from Bob, followed by the call from Zoe's school, forced Ann to recognise that she was not coping.

But there was another important factor: Cheryl's determined encouragement and advice, telling Ann she was entitled to help. This draws attention to the importance of friends as part of family care networks.

In Unit 3, you will learn what happened when Ann's plea for help was eventually answered.

2.6 The complexities of caring

Although care relationships are sometimes rewarding, especially when there is genuine affection, and a positive history to draw on, they can also be stressful for both parties. As you saw in Section 2.2, the experience of being in long-term caring situations is influenced by a number of factors, including the quality of the relationship, how much choice people have in becoming a carer and in how they do the caring, and the amount and type of support available to carers from family, friends and outside agencies.

On the other side of the coin, people who are cared for can experience very negative feelings about being a burden, and about loss of independence and loss of opportunities. As has been mentioned, they can also be vulnerable to abuse. Poverty makes things worse, by reducing people's choices further. Caring does not have to be as negative as this, but people need support, encouragement and practical assistance if they are to retain sufficient control over important aspects of their lives.

Key points

- Care relationships can be stressful and demanding.

- The quality of the relationship between the person who is cared for and the carer is influenced by the dynamics of family life, past and present.

- Lack of information about alternatives, and a sense of duty, often means that family members do not feel they have a choice about taking on the role of carer.

- It often takes a crisis before people ask for support.

- The situation of people on the receiving end of care mirrors that of carers in many respects. In addition, however, they are vulnerable to abuse or ill-treatment from their carers in the privacy of the home.

Learning skills: Managing time

You have now completed two of the four sections of Unit 1. How are you doing for time? How long have you spent so far? Has it been one session of study, or several? What times of the day seem to work best for you? Will you be able to fit the rest of the unit into this week? Will you still have time for the short practice essay at the end (about two hours)?

These are challenging questions. Everyone finds time management difficult, especially when taking on something new. To get some ideas on fitting K101 into your week, have a look at *The Good Study Guide*, Sections 2.3.2 to 2.3.4 (pages 34–40). Then try setting yourself a target time for finishing Section 3 of this unit. Look in the unit contents list to see how many pages Section 3 contains. Guess how many minutes you take per page, and see how close you get.

Reader

3 Putting the case study in context

You have considered one family's experience of caring. But how typical is this? In this section, you will consider this question using two different sources of evidence:

- statistics on how many people are carers

- research into the experiences of another group of people who are involved in caring.

3.1 Carers: some facts

How many people are in Ann's position? As you know already, this is not an easy question to answer because many people who are carers do not label themselves as such. But since 1985, efforts have been made to count the number of people who care. A question on caring responsibilities was included in the 2001 National Census of all households in the UK. People were asked if they provided care, and if so, what they did and how many hours a week they provided care for. In the box below, you will find the information the census yielded about the extent of caring in the UK in 2001.

Carers

How many people are carers?

The 2001 UK census found that 6 million people said they provide unpaid care to a family member; in other words, 12% of the adult population. Of these:

- 68% (3.56 million) said they provide care for up to 19 hours a week.

- 11% (0.57 million) said they provide care for 20 to 49 hours.

- 21% (1.9 million) said they provide care for over 50 hours per week.

(Source: based on Office of Population Censuses and Surveys, 2001)

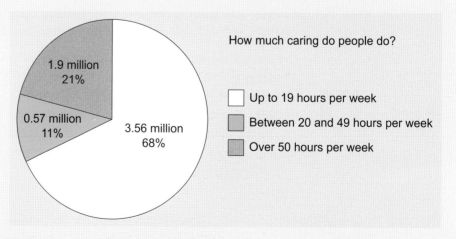

Figure 1   How much caring do people do? (Source: based on Office of Population Censuses and Surveys, 2001)

These figures mask differences in the four UK nations. In Wales, 16% of the population describe themselves as carers, in Scotland 12%, and in one study in Northern Ireland, 18% of people reported themselves to be carers, with 6% caring for over 20 hours a week.

Who are the carers?

The census in 2001 identified 3.4 million women, and 2.46 million men. In percentage terms:

- 58% of carers are women
- 42% are men.

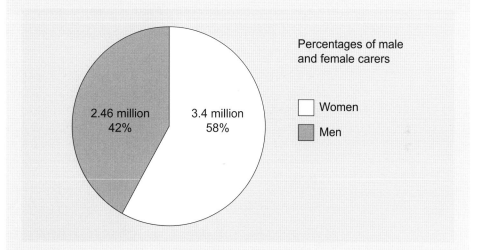

Figure 2   Percentages of male and female carers (Source: based on Office of Population Censuses and Surveys, 2001)

This difference has not changed since statistics on caring began to be collected in the 1980s. Again, the figures mask some significant differences. For example, in Scotland 62% of carers are women and 38% are men.

The peak age for caring is 50 to 59. More than 1 in 5 of the population in this age bracket provide care.

Researchers estimate that 175,000 young people, under the age of 18, are carers, of whom 13,029 provide care for more than 50 hours a week.

(Source: based on Office of Population Censuses and Surveys, 2001)

What do carers do?

- 51% look after someone with whom they share a home, providing personal care such as bathing, washing, dressing, toileting.
- 57% provide help with mobility – getting in and out of bed, walking, using stairs.
- 22% give medicines.
- 71% provide 'other help'.

Who do carers care for?

- 70% of people at the receiving end of (family) care are over the age of 65.
- 38% of carers care for parents.
- 18% of carers care for spouses or partners.

(Source: based on Carers UK, 2005)

Learning skills: Working with numbers

There are quite a lot of numbers to take in here. What do you do when you come across numbers, percentages and charts as you are reading? Do you stop to take in what they mean, or do you skip ahead and carry on reading? In a course like this, you will miss a great deal if you do skip. Numbers can tell you a lot very quickly. You may be quite comfortable with numbers, in which case this box isn't for you. But if you aren't, we shall aim to help you in K101 by:

- bringing numbers and charts into the course a bit at a time, starting with simple ones
- giving you advice and practice with reading charts
- asking you to read some easy figures from charts as part of your assignment work.

You can make a start by going back over the box above, picking out a few numbers (say, five) that you think are particularly useful to know, and highlighting them.

Activity 9   Is Ann a 'typical' carer?

Allow about 20 minutes

Consider Ann's situation in the light of the information in the box on 'Carers' above. How typical is she?

Consider this question under the following headings:

(a) Her gender

(b) Her age

(c) Her relationship with the person she cares for

(d) The care she provides

(e) How much caring she does.

Comment

(a) **Her gender**. In being a woman, Ann is in the majority. As mentioned earlier, although the difference between the extent of caring by men and women is not enormous (58 carers in 100 are women as against 42 in 100 men), most men care for partners rather than parents (Evandrou, 1990). In early studies of caring, it was thought that caring was almost exclusively women's work. Lewis and Meredith, in their 1988 study *Daughters Who Care*, surmised that this referred partly to those women who were single and who had never left home, and were therefore there to do the caring. It is still the case that when a younger person cares for an older person, or where there is a disabled child needing care, it is usually women who take it on.

(b) **Her age**. At thirty-seven, Ann is younger than the most typical age for caring – as you have seen, the peak age for caring is when people are in their fifties.

(c) **Her relationship with the person she cares for**. Thirty-eight carers in every 100 care for parents, so there are plenty of people like Ann. Most people who are cared for (seventy in every 100) are, like Angus, over the age of sixty-five.

(d) **The care she provides**. Ann is like most carers in providing help with personal care (51%) and mobility (57%). Only a minority (22%) administer medicines.

(e) **How much caring she does**. Ann does more than most carers. She cares for at least thirty-five hours a week, putting her in the top 32%. She also gives medicines, which only twenty-two in 100 carers do.

This exercise in comparing Ann with national statistics indicates that although her situation is in many senses unique, there are many people in similar situations. So, although the case study focuses on just one family, their situation is not so very unusual.

3.2 Experiencing care as a younger person

So far, the focus has been on care where an older person is the person needing support, using the case study. To give you a sense of the similarities, and the differences, when young people need care, we now consider the situation of younger disabled adults and children whose families find themselves in the complex role of carer.

Activity 10   Young, and disabled
Allow about 20 minutes

Read the following extracts from a research study by Yasmin Hussain, Karl Atkin and Waqar Ahmad published in 2002. They interviewed disabled Asian people in their teens and twenties about their experiences. (The information in parentheses refers to the page numbers in the book where the quotations can be found.)

Then make some notes on what you learned about what it is like as a younger person to be cared for within the family. Use the following headings for your notes:

(a) Feeling a burden

(b) Fear

(c) Isolation

(d) Choice.

Then note anything which struck you about the similarities, and the differences, between what the young people say and what you know about Angus.

Nasira:

> They help me a lot. And you know, they'll do a lot for me. My family supports me 100%. They make life easier for me. And I've got a family; I don't really need anybody else, do I? They care for me really a lot. (p. 11)

However, Nasira also commented:

> I don't have any friends because I don't go anywhere, therefore I don't have any friends. They don't come around because I'm disabled, you see, they don't want to know me. (p. 19)

Waheed, aged 27:

> Obviously when my younger sister gets married, obviously she'll have to leave and my parents, my father is already 63 and my mum is 50 something and when they pass away, I'll be on my own and I hate to be alone. And that really does choke me sometimes. (p. 13)

Fatima, aged 28:

> Sometimes it's good, you know, you get all the attention and you get everything done for you and then at other times, you wish you know, they wouldn't go on about it. (p. 18)

Jamila, aged 22, speaking of a meeting with a social worker:

> I just wanted some information, you know, I was just deciding whether to move out and have my own place and he was like really putting me off ... saying ... you know, it's really hard work ... then you become lonely and stuff. (p. 25)

Gurupal, aged 28:

> I think my disability is restricting because they [parents] are more protective of what I do ... They seem very reluctant to let me have my freedom and sort of let me go in that respect. And I just want them to be more understanding and allow me to be my own person really. (p. 18)

> I really had to stamp my foot down and say 'Mum, I respect your opinion and I appreciate what you're saying and I'm taking this on board', but I mean I can't be stuck in the house for all of my life and staring at four walls, I have to socialise and interact with people, because that is the only way I'm going to develop as a person. (p. 7)

Comment

Here are my notes.

(a) **Feeling a burden**. No one mentioned this. However, Fatima and Nasira commented on feeling both loved and also over-protected and constrained by their families.

(b) **Fear**. Waheed was scared of a future when his parents would no longer be there for him.

(c) **Isolation**. This was mentioned by Nasira, Waheed and Jamila, while Gurupal emphasised how important it was for him to get out and socialise.

(d) **Choice**. Only one of the young people quoted here (Jamila) mentioned that they had any choice about remaining within the care of their families. Gurupal reported that he had asserted his need to get out and socialise – he had made some choices within the context of family care. The rest seemed resigned to the life they were living.

The big difference that struck me in comparison with Angus was that these young people have a lifetime ahead of them, and have to consider a future without their parents' love and support, whereas Angus, at the other end of life, probably did not dwell on that likelihood. The importance these young people accorded to friendship is another difference, although, like me, you may well think Angus would have benefited from some good friends.

Activity 11   The view from the other side
Allow about 20 minutes

In this activity you will consider the other side of the relationship, looking at extracts from the same research study by Hussain et al. (2002), this time giving parents' perspectives, along with that of a sister. Use these headings to make some notes:

(a) Feelings about being a carer

(b) The amount of support they receive from others.

Moeen's mother:

> I know there are carers that are available, but I want to look after Moeen myself. As far as I am concerned, as long as God gives me the energy to look after my son, I will. I don't want anybody else coming here and looking after my son. (p. 26)

Gurucharan's mother:

> He might think low of himself by saying that other people have to come and help. We therefore feel it is important that he knows we care. (p. 26)

Jagjeet's mother:

> I made a big mistake by doing everything for her, so now, it's not her fault, it's all my fault that I've made it too easy for her. (p. 17)

Tahir's mother:

> I try to make him independent. I think that is where a lot of mothers went wrong and they give the child everything. If they don't give the child everything, they've got to go and get it and that encourages the child to get up and go. (p. 10)

> If anything happens to him now, I don't know what I would do. I don't. I would be really lost. I really would be lost. (p. 11)

> I've been coping for six years. It's difficult to go through. Don't ask me where I've got the strength, I don't know. I just hope I've got the strength to carry on. Sometimes I've felt like, forget him, run away, but you can't, you cannot run away from it. It is impossible. They are your children and you have to look after them. (p. 11)

Rabia's father:

> Here children do not look after their parents, let alone their sisters, do they? Don't get me wrong, all her brothers and sisters, all would give their life for her, they love her even more than us. But it's not the same as it used to be. Those from Pakistan would look after people like Rabia. People born here are very reluctant to do that. (p. 10)

Sushma's sister:

> Everyone else is scared that she might break something and so will
> anticipate the worse and she went to my aunt's house the other day and
> everyone like said, 'why did you bring her, why did you bring her?' (p. 13)

Comment

(a) **Feelings about being a carer**. There is a real mixture here. Love for her
child, accompanied by a strong sense of duty, is expressed most clearly by
Tahir's mother. Here the idea that caring about someone means you must
care *for* them is clearly expressed. This can become a 'burden', as Tahir's
mother's comment indicates.

Two of the mothers (Moeen's and Gurucharan's) were aware that they were
making a choice to care, rather than seek alternatives. But both also felt that
their offspring would think less of them if they did not do the caring – like Ann,
they felt a strong sense of family duty. Tahir's mother did not recognise that
she had a choice – she just had to struggle on.

The other theme I noticed was the need to help the child become more
independent: not to do everything for them. Jagjeet's mother reckoned she
had got this wrong.

(b) **The amount of support they receive from others**. Several of the mothers
mentioned the lack of support from the wider family, and Rabia's father made
negative comparisons with practice in Pakistan where, he felt, the family would
have been more supportive. It does not sound as if Jagjeet's mother had had
support in helping her daughter build her own independence, although she
blamed herself for making the mistake of doing everything for her.

Reading these accounts, I noticed that unlike Ann, several of the mothers
recognised that they should help their son or daughter become more
independent, because they knew that they themselves would not always
be on hand. Another theme was that these (mostly) first-generation Asian
migrants contrasted the support they got from wider family in the UK with life
back in Pakistan.

This study of the experiences of a particular group of families suggests that there
are parallels between care in families where there is an older person who is sick
and frail, and the experiences of families where there is a young disabled person.

There are also big differences. Several of the young people were asserting their
need to develop their own independence. One was actively seeking alternatives
to living at home. Several mothers also recognised that they should be looking
ahead and fostering their children's independence. At no point so far has Ann
apparently considered whether she could do more to give Angus some control
over his life.

There are alternatives for these young people and their parents. Jamila was
actively pursuing her options to move out and live independently. There are
options, also, for Angus and Ann, but when people are caught up in the day-
to-day routine of managing under difficult circumstances, they may have little
energy to pursue them. You will learn more about these options as you work
through the course.

This study happened to be about Asian families. Perhaps you wondered whether that made a difference to the experience of caring. The researchers who undertook this study argued that Asian families get less support from formal services than do White British people, and the support is less appropriate (Hussain et al., 2002). The impact of being from a minority ethnic background and needing care is explored in more depth in Unit 2.

3.3 Care and your family

To encourage you to actively think about the themes explored in this unit so far, the next activity asks you to consider your own family's experience of care and caring in the light of these themes.

Activity 12   Your family?

Allow about 15 minutes

Take a few moments to consider care in your own family. If there is a frail older person, or a younger person who requires support to manage everyday life:

- Who does the caring?
- Do they recognise themselves as a carer?
- What is the quality of the relationship?
- How much choice have people had to be in this relationship?
- Where does support come from?
- Is there reciprocity?

If you do not have any such situations in your own family, consider other families you know.

Comment

We asked people who read the course in draft to let us use their examples.

Jessica wrote:

> My sister has Motor Neurone disease. Her carer is her husband. He has made a definite choice to care for her, and when offered Carer's Allowance rejected it as insulting. Her condition is worsening rapidly, now she can barely walk even with someone supporting her on either side. He really wants to support her to have a life of her own, and used to encourage her to email me and her friends, but now she cannot use a keyboard. I find it very hard as I live 200 miles away and work full time. I'd love to be nearer so I could help more on a day to day basis. Instead I rely on phoning him, and visiting once a month at a weekend which I find exhausting, mentally and physically. I cannot imagine how he feels, living with the strain and the sadness day after day.

> The situation works because he is devoted to her, despite her having been ill with depression and now this. He gets support (not enough) from friends, from me, from our elderly parents, and from Social Services after a long struggle.

> I don't think there is reciprocity now, but there used to be, when she was well.

Catherine wrote of a very different example:

> As a career woman living alone care has not come into my life much (except the cat). But last year one of my friends had a hip replacement and she organised three of us to do two or three day shifts. I was surprised at how difficult it was. Yes, I chose to respond positively to the request, and yes, our relationship was a strong one – or she would not have asked me – but I was a guest in her house, wanting to do things her way and not offend. My instinct was to race over and do things for her – but how much should I stand back and wait to be asked? I wanted to support her autonomy, but had a sneaking feeling she might think me lazy when I shut myself away with the work I had brought, asking her to give me a shout if she wanted anything. Did I get it wrong? I don't really know.
>
> As for reciprocity, when she thanked me I found myself jokingly saying this was fine, it put me in credit for when I needed care.

The course readers observed how much they had learned through being asked to reflect on their experience of care in the light of the themes in this unit. Did you learn anything new and surprising?

Key points

- The case study is not 'typical', but there are many families in a similar position.
- The majority of carers are women, and most people cared for are older.
- The experience of caring varies when the people who are at the receiving end are young people, but there are many common themes.

Reader

Learning skills: Managing time

Did you reach your target time for Section 3? Did the activities hold you up longer than expected? Do you need to adjust your strategy for managing time? Perhaps it would be worth looking back at pages 34–40 of *The Good Study Guide* and re-examining your strategy.

You don't need to be able to estimate time precisely, or become obsessed with achieving targets. But you need to be aware of study time as something that requires management. You need to develop a feel for what kinds of things use up most time and where you can catch up time if you need to.

4 Changing families, changing care

Although care has been part of family life and human relationships since time immemorial, it is only relatively recently that carers inside families have become the subject of much public attention. Before the last quarter of the twentieth century, carers were pretty invisible. As researchers Bill Bytheway and Julia Johnson comment:

> It is perhaps difficult to appreciate that less than forty years ago, the term carer was barely in the English language.

> (Bytheway and Johnson, 1998, p. 241)

If care was going on in families anyway, why is interest in carers so recent?

Families have changed dramatically over the past half century. More divorce, smaller families, greater numbers of people living alone, families scattered across the country and across the globe, more women in paid work – all these have had an impact on the family's capacity to care.

In order to consider this, I am going to introduce you to two studies of one geographical area in England: Bethnal Green in East London. One study, *The Family Life of Older People* by Peter Townsend, was conducted in the mid-1950s. The other, *The New East End: Kinship, Race and Conflict* by Geoff Dench, Kate Gavron and Michael Young, was conducted between 1992 and 2005. The reason for choosing Bethnal Green is essentially a practical one – that we have accurate information from these two studies, which enables comparisons to be made between families then and now.

4.1 Changing families: family life in the 1950s

To gain an insight into families in the 1950s, we turn to Peter Townsend's *The Family Life of Older People*, published in 1957. Townsend tried to understand society through a series of research studies, particularly into ageing.

He explains the purpose of this particular study thus:

> We often suppose old people are more isolated than in the past. Is this true? There are hints it is not. The question is important and answering it is likely to show better how to meet the social, medical and economic needs of old age … The book is largely based on intensive interviews with a random sample of 200 old people in Bethnal Green, London.

> (Townsend, 1957, p. x)

Townsend did not say that he was going to find out about caring. However, as you will see, his study does shed light on care and caring.

Townsend wanted to find out what is really going on in communities as a basis for meeting 'the social, medical and economic needs of old age', and putting services in place which actually support families to care. As mentioned, he did this by selecting a small geographical area, Bethnal Green in East London, which then housed about 54,000 people (Townsend, 1957, p. 12), and selecting around 200 people to study in depth.

So what did Townsend and his research team find out? The case study we have chosen can be found in Chapter 1 in the Reader, and you should turn to this now, in preparation for an activity in which you will practise note taking.

Reader

Activity 13   The family life of older people in the 1950s

Allow about 15 minutes

Turn to Chapter 1, 'Anthology: people', compiled by Ken Blakemore and Joanna Bornat in the Reader, and read the extract there entitled 'Mrs Bliss' (pages 12–13). Make some notes for yourself on the way in which care was provided to Mrs Bliss during her final illness.

Comment

- Mrs Bliss lived with her 'now very infirm' husband. He attended to some 'personal needs'.
- Her five children organised a rota to sleep over, two taking the main responsibility.
- They also jointly ensured that the shopping and cleaning were done.
- Family members brought food, flowers, sheets and blankets.
- The sons and daughters shared news via telephone boxes on a constant basis.

Did you get these points?

Reader

Learning skills: Highlighting and underlining as you read

As you read about Mrs Bliss, did you highlight or underline important words? It's a way of making reading a more active process which engages your mind. But how much should you highlight or underline? To get a few ideas and find out what other students think, go to page 118 of *The Good Study Guide* and read from the heading 'Too much underlining and highlighting' to the end of Section 5.5.3 on page 120.

Townsend found plenty of examples of this kind of shared care across family members in his study of the family life of older people in Bethnal Green in the 1950s. Such sharing made care for very sick people more bearable. It was made possible because:

- 46% of the older people he interviewed lived with younger relatives.
- Most others had relatives living nearby.
- The 200 people interviewed had between them 2,700 relatives living within a mile, an average of over ten per person. One had ninety relatives within a mile.
- 85% of those with children had an adult child living within a mile.

- Very few adult children had moved far from their parents – only 11% did not live in or around London.

- People kept in frequent contact – only 4% did not see one of their children once a week, and 78% saw a son or a daughter every day.

- Until they became seriously ill, older women, in particular, were able to reciprocate the care they received from younger relatives, by cooking meals or looking after grandchildren.

Townsend showed that a major factor in older people's lives when they became ill was the presence of relatives, particularly their children, living within easy reach, and that there was a lot of reciprocity across the generations. He summed up:

> Old people get much help from their relatives, help which is reciprocated [paid back]. The two-way traffic is an essential feature of the family.

> (Townsend, 1957, p. xi)

This finding, that care is a two-way thing, is echoed in Forbat's much more recent study of care relationships. She notes:

> There is reciprocity in many care relationships, which may fluctuate across generations, and indeed from day to day.

> (Forbat, 2005, p. 27)

However, we should not get too much of a rosy glow about life in 1950s East London. Not everyone had family help. People without children, or willing nieces and nephews, nearby, did not do so well.

Townsend noted:

> Those with no available relatives were in the worst position.

> (Townsend, 1957, p. 46)

At the end of his book, Townsend came to the conclusion that without what we now call family care, and what he called 'the care given by female relatives', the demands on services would be enormous. The people least likely to make demands on state-provided services for older people were those with daughters at hand. The greatest demands were made by 'elderly isolates': people who had no relatives to support them (p. 206).

So, although Townsend's study did not set out to find out about caring, it tells us a lot about it. It found carers, even if it didn't call them that. Here are the main points about caring that come from the study:

- Most care was done by female relatives: daughters, daughters-in-law, sometimes nieces. Grandchildren also feature.

- One person – usually a daughter – was the main person who provided the care.

- Care was made easier by families living near one another, making it possible for frequent, often daily, contact.

- There was reciprocity – older people repaid the care they were given by younger generations, particularly by preparing meals and looking after grandchildren.

- People without relatives were the most likely to need state support.
- Improving the family's ability to provide care was the right way for state services to go.

I started this section by asking why family carers had only become of interest to policy makers since the latter part of the twentieth century, when they were self-evidently there all along. Townsend's findings suggest an answer – caring was such an integral part of family life that it could be taken for granted, there was nothing out of the ordinary about it, and it did not need to be made into a public issue except for the few who lacked family. If Bethnal Green was like other parts of the country, most care would just go on being provided by families, with only a few falling outside the net.

4.2 Families and caring: Bethnal Green in the late twentieth century

So what has changed – and what is the same? Do families still care? Or have the fears expressed by Townsend – that older people are more isolated than in the past – come to pass?

Geoff Dench, Kate Gavron and Michael Young revisited Bethnal Green (now part of the London Borough of Tower Hamlets) during the 1990s. Like Townsend, they used random sampling of residents as their main source of information, along with local newspapers and reports.

The biggest change of all that they reported was in the ethnic composition of the Borough, with people of Bangladeshi origin comprising one-third of the population in 2001, and three-fifths of the school enrolments (Dench et al., 2006, p. 15). However, in order to see the changes to family life for people from similar backgrounds to those studied by Townsend fifty years earlier, and thus to make a comparison between the two studies, we will explore that part of the research by Dench et al. which looked at the changes experienced by older white women, illustrated by the quotations below.

> There are a lot of lonely old people around here who don't see a soul. A lot of old people moved out with the GLC [Greater London Council]. They had the chance of a one-bedroom flat come up. And their children have moved as well, so the family breaks up.
>
> […]
>
> My brothers and sisters moved out, so I don't see so much of them now. They've bought their own houses and they've moved out, but if we need help they're here straight away. It's not as it used to be. People were much closer years ago. When people were poor they kept closer together. People are moving away from the area, so families are bound to break up.
>
> […]
>
> There are too many youngsters leaving home now. There isn't a grandmother or an auntie for children to fall back on …
>
> (Dench et al., 2006, pp. 116, 117)

The people quoted here offer explanations of how family life has changed, with people leaving the area to buy their own homes.

Statistical evidence supports the views expressed here that families have dispersed. You will recall that for the 200 people Townsend interviewed, there was an average of ten relatives living within one mile. Dench et al. provide similar information about what they term 'local family network density' for the 530 white people in their survey (see Table 1).

Table 1   Local family network density in Tower Hamlets, 2001

No relatives nearby	Some: 1 or 2 relatives nearby	Dense: 3 or more relatives nearby	Total
177	198	155	530

(Source: adapted from Dench et al., 2006, p. 239)

Table 1 tells us that 177 of the 530 people interviewed by Dench et al. had no relatives (outside their immediate household) within the Borough of Tower Hamlets. We can state this more powerfully by calling it around one-third. One hundred and ninety-eight, or just over one-third, had one or two relatives, and 155, or just under one-third, had three or more nearby relatives. This tells us that at the beginning of the twenty-first century, people's families were more scattered than they had been in the mid-twentieth century, in this part of East London.

In relation to capacity to care, the figures suggest to me that the type of shared family care that was described by Townsend is much less likely now. This tallies with the comments from the interviewees in the Dench study about lonely older people, and there being no grandmothers and aunties to fall back on.

The findings in this study indicate very substantial changes in family life in this part of East London. The close-knit extended families familiar from Townsend's study were fast disappearing in the white community fifty years later. The reasons for this are many, and associated with changes in the economy, in housing policy and in people's individual wealth. Whether it means that families no longer care as much for their relatives is the question to ponder in the final part of this unit.

4.3 Do families still care?

This is a very difficult question to answer. Two researchers who considered whether families still cared thirty years on from the 1950s were Hazel Qureshi and Alan Walker. After extensive investigation into families with frail older relatives in England, they found no evidence to support the view that families no longer cared. They wrote:

> We were struck, first, by the universal nature of the acceptance of their [sons' and daughters'] primary role in care for elderly relatives and second, by the tremendous normative pressures on them to do so.

(Qureshi and Walker, 1989, p. 2)

In this quotation the term 'normative pressures' refers to the strong expectations of others that families were responsible for caring for their relatives when they needed support.

Other researchers who have considered this issue include Chris Phillipson and colleagues who conclude that compared with Townsend's day:

> ... talking about *the* family life of older people has become a more complex task. There are many more different 'types' of older people ...

and many more different types of families … But the family in some
form is still central to support in later life, even if this is often focused
around a small number of network members.

(Phillipson et al., 2002, p. 119)

This view was reinforced by Emily Grundy, a researcher at the London School
for Hygiene and Tropical Medicine, who found little research evidence to
support the view that families are less willing to care for relatives than in the past
(National Statistics, 2006). In other words, most family members seem to accept
that they have a responsibility to their older relatives. It is just that with many
families far more scattered than they were in the past, and with smaller families
anyway, the practicalities of managing care have become that much more
challenging, and fall to a fewer number of relatives – as in this unit's case study
of Ann and Angus. These changes in family life help to explain why interest
in carers has grown, with a recognition that efforts need to be made to support
people like Ann.

4.4 What does it all mean for caring?

In this final section of Unit 1, you have been considering why informal care in
families came to public attention towards the end of the twentieth century. The focus
was on changes in family life, about which Townsend's study of the family life of
older people gives some clues. When different generations of families lived together
in relatively stable communities, families could be relied on to provide care for their
older relatives. One relative, usually a daughter, would take the lead responsibility,
but other relatives helped out too. Except for the minority without family at hand,
not much help was needed from public services, except medical services.

As these settled patterns change, as more people move away to find better homes,
to study and take jobs, and more women take jobs outside the home, so the
family's capacity to care in the way it did in 1950s Bethnal Green also changes.
Families still play a central role, but far fewer family members are involved,
and, in many cases, there are great distances to cover. This seems to lead to the
sorts of caring situations highlighted in the case study, and in the study of young
disabled people, where one person takes on responsibility and there is very little
support from elsewhere, except from public services.

Why have carers become a matter of public rather than private interest? The fear
is that unless better support is available to help people carry on caring, costs to
the public purse of providing care will be immense.

Key points

- Although caring has long been done within families, it only became a matter
  of public interest in the late twentieth century.

- In some communities in the mid-twentieth century, care was accomplished by
  a network of family members living near to one another. Daughters usually
  took the main responsibility for caring.

- Changes in the way families live have led to caring becoming less of a
  shared responsibility between family members.

- However, there is little evidence that families have rejected the idea that they
  have a responsibility to care for family members as they grow old and frail,
  but smaller families and greater distances mean that the type of contact has
  changed.

Conclusion

In Unit 1 you have explored care within families. You have moved from a single case study ('Ann and Angus') to consider whether this is representative of caring experiences more widely. You have considered why family care is important, and why policy makers and others are interested in it.

In the rest of Block 1 you will be learning about formal care services, where professionals and paid workers do the work of caring.

Learning skills: Using the end-of-unit checklist

At the end of each of the first three units in every block you will find a checklist which will help you to check whether you have grasped the main ideas from that unit. It will also give you an idea of what you might be asked to write about in an assignment or an exam.

Core questions

The core questions at the start of each of the first three units in every block do the same kind of thing. However, they are intended to set you up beforehand, so that you can see in what direction the unit will be heading and what kinds of things you will be thinking about. The core questions are written in everyday language on the understanding that you haven't yet got to grips with the topic, whereas the end-of-unit checklist uses the language you have met in the unit and pulls things together in more formal terms.

Investing in your learning skills

Reader

K101 is going to keep raising learning skills issues and setting you tasks to develop your learning skills, so it is important to pause and consider how much of your energy you should use in this way. To help you reflect on this, your final reading for Unit 1 is *The Good Study Guide*, Sections 1.1 to 1.4 (pages 9–18).

Difficult personal issues

Perhaps some of what you have read in Unit 1 has touched very close to your own experiences, past or present, in ways that were difficult or upsetting to think about. Caring situations often have stressful or painful aspects. It is particularly important that a course like K101 recognises these issues and discusses them, using real cases to help draw out just why particular situations can be difficult and what might be done to help. The course writers have tried very hard to discuss all issues sensitively and responsibly, but it is possible that at some point you will come to a case, or a discussion, which arouses emotions you have difficulty coping with. If this happens, and you feel you need to stop reading the topic under discussion and move on to the next section of the course, you should feel free to do so – although you might want to consult your tutor first. Alternatively, you might feel the need to talk to a friend, a counsellor or a helpline. Perhaps it would be a good idea to think now about who that would be.

Practice essay

Your last piece of work for Unit 1 is to write a very short essay just to make contact with your tutor and get yourself started on the writing part of your studies. This counts for only a quarter of the marks of a normal assignment, so think of it as a practice run. You will receive advice back from your tutor, which will be very helpful when you reach the first proper assignment in four weeks' time at the end of Block 1. For full details of what to do, find TMA 01 in the Assessment Guide.

End-of-unit checklist

Now you have completed Unit 1, you should be able to:

- explain the concept of family care

- explain the significance of family care within overall care provision and link it to national care policy

- outline some of the key challenges associated with family care

- explain why family care has become the subject of government attention in recent years.

References

Bytheway, B. and Johnson, J. (1998) 'The social construction of "carers"' in Symonds, A. and Kelly, A. (eds) *The Social Construction of Community Care*, London, Macmillan.

Carers National Association (2001) *You Can Take Him Home Now*, London, Carers National Association.

Carers UK (2003) *Missed Opportunities*, London, Carers UK.

Carers UK (2005) *Facts about Carers*, London, Carers UK; also available online at www.carersuk.org/Policyandpractice/PolicyResources/Policybriefings/ factsaboutcarers2005.pdf (Accessed 25 February 2008).

Carers UK (2006) [online], www.carersuk.org (Accessed 25 February 2008).

Cavaye, J. (2007) *Policy and Practice in Health and Social Care: Hidden Carers*, Dunedin, Dunedin Academic Press.

Dench, G., Gavron, K. and Young, M. (2006) *The New East End: Kinship, Race and Conflict*, London, Profile Books.

Department of Health (DH) (1999) *Caring about Carers: A National Strategy for Carers*, London, The Stationery Office; also available online at www.dh.gov.uk/en/Publicationsandstatistics/Publications/ PublicationsPolicyAndGuidance/DH_4006522 (Accessed 25 February 2008).

Department of Health (DH) (2000) *National Strategy for Carers*, London, The Stationery Office.

Department of Health (DH) (2006) *Our Health, Our Care, Our Say: A New Direction for Community Services*, London, The Stationery Office.

Directgov (2006) *Introduction to Caring* [online], www.direct.gov.uk/en/CaringForSomeone/CaringAndSupportServices/DG_ 10016779 (Accessed 22 January 2008).

Directgov (2007) *Carers and Employment* [online], www.direct.gov.uk/en/CaringForSomeone/CarersRights/DG_4001078 (Accessed 28 January 2008).

ePolitix.com (2007) *The Open University Tops Student Satisfaction Ratings for Third Year Running* [online], www.epolitix.com/NR/exeres/77057E62-6070-41DE-91CC-E7E5BEADC131 (Accessed 28 January 2008).

Evandrou, M. (1990) *Challenging the Invisibility of Carers: Mapping Informal Care Nationally*, London, London School of Economics.

Finch, J. (1989) *Family Obligations and Social Change*, Cambridge, Polity Press.

Finch, J. and Mason, J. (1992) *Negotiating Family Responsibilities*, London, Tavistock/ Routledge.

Fine, M. (2007) *A Caring Society? Care and the Dilemmas of Human Service in the 21st Century*, London, Palgrave.

Forbat, E. (2005) *Talking about Care: Two Sides to the Story*, Bristol, The Policy Press.

House of Commons Health Committee (2004) *Elder Abuse: Second Report of Session 2003–4*, London, The Stationery Office.

Hussain, Y., Atkin, K. and Ahmad, W. (2002) *South Asian Disabled Young People and Their Families*, Bristol, The Policy Press/Joseph Rowntree Foundation.

Jones, C. and Rupp, S. (2000) 'Understanding the carers' world: a biographical interpretive case study' in Chamberlayne, P., Bornat, J. and Wengraf, T. (eds) *The Turn to Biographical Methods in Social Science*, London, Routledge.

Laing, W. (2005) *Trends in the London Care Market 1994–2024*, London, King's Fund.

Lewis, J. and Meredith, B. (1988) *Daughters Who Care*, London, Routledge.

Morris, J. (1993) *Independent Lives*, London, Macmillan.

National Statistics (2006) 'Report of joint ESRC/ONS/BSPS public policy seminar on the implications of demographic change', *Population Trends*, 125, pp. 98–103.

Office of Population Censuses and Surveys (2001) *National Census*, London, The Stationery Office; also available online at www.statistics.gov.uk/StatBase/ssdataset.asp?vlnk=7396& Pos=1& ColRank=1& Rank=272 (Accessed 25 February 2008).

Parker, G. and Lawton, D. (1994) *Different Types of Care, Different Types of Carer*, London, HMSO.

Parkinson's Disease Society (2005) *Parkinson's and You*, London, Parkinson's Disease Society; also available online at www.parkinsons.org.uk/PDF/pub_p2_parkinsons_you_06.pdf (Accessed 18 December 2007).

Phillipson, C., Bernard, M., Phillips, J. and Ogg, J. (2002) 'Social change, networks and family life' in Bytheway, B., Bacigalupo, V., Bornat, J., Johnson, J. and Spurr, S. (eds) *Understanding Care, Welfare and Community: A Reader*, London, Routledge.

Qureshi, H. and Walker, A. (1989) *The Caring Relationship: Elderly People and Their Families*, London, Macmillan.

The Pension Service (2007) [online], www.thepensionservice.gov.uk/planningahead/glossary.asp (Accessed 22 January 2008).

Townsend, P. (1957) *The Family Life of Older People: An Inquiry in East London*, London, Routledge and Kegan Paul.

Website

www.directgov.uk (Accessed 25 February 2008).

Unit 2
Illness, health and care

Prepared for the course team by Naomi Anna Watson and Andrew Northedge

Contents

Introduction

Health, wealth and happiness are what people wish for others. Health ranks as one of the supremely important goals in life. And it is always in the news. Here are some headlines from a random day:

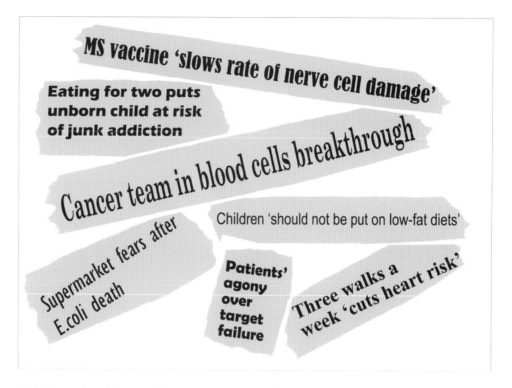

MS vaccine 'slows rate of nerve cell damage'

Eating for two puts unborn child at risk of junk addiction

Cancer team in blood cells breakthrough

Supermarket fears after E.coli death

Children 'should not be put on low-fat diets'

Patients' agony over target failure

Three walks a week 'cuts heart risk'

Behind the headlines millions of people work in the cause of health. Over 1.3 million work for the National Health Service (NHS) and many others work in private health clinics, or as dentists, opticians, fitness coaches, and so on. And as you know from Unit 1, millions of people care for the health of family members and friends. Moreover, most people spend some time each day caring for their own health – brushing their teeth, taking exercise, considering their diet. So health care is a core activity within our society.

But are we really sure what we mean by health and illness? And how can we try to make sense of the vast range of health care activities going on in society – particularly as health care is continually changing? This unit sets out to map the main forms of health care provision in the UK and to explore how and why they are changing. As with Unit 1, a central case study provides focus and brings issues down to the everyday reality of people's lives.

Core questions

- What are the implications of being ill?
- How are health care services provided in the community, particularly for people with long-term health concerns?
- How can health care services ensure that they meet the needs of the great variety of people who use them?
- Why are some kinds of health care provided in hospitals, and what are the implications of being treated, or working, in hospital?
- How are health care services changing and why?

Are you taking the IVR?

If you are studying K101 as part of the Integrated Vocational Route (IVR), don't forget to check your VQ Candidate Handbook to see which Unit 2 activities contribute to your electronic portfolio.

1 Being ill

We begin by exploring what illness means. What makes people decide they are ill – and what do they do about it, when they think they are?

1.1 What does 'being ill' mean?

Since nearly everyone has experiences of being ill, a good place to begin is to think about what *you* mean when you describe yourself as ill.

Activity 1   What is your idea of 'being ill'?

Allow about 10 minutes

Have you been ill recently? Were you often ill as a child? Write down two or three examples of times when you have been ill. (If you prefer, think about illnesses of people you know.)

For each example write a few notes in answer to these questions:

(a) How did you know that you were ill?

(b) What were the consequences of deciding that you were ill? (What did you or other people do about it?)

Comment

Here are answers from some people I asked.

- One person remembered that as a boy he couldn't be ill if he didn't 'have a temperature'. His mother would put a thermometer in his mouth and if his temperature was normal, then up he had to get for school. But if his temperature was high, he had to stay in bed until the thermometer reading was back down. If it stayed high for more than a day there would be a trip to the doctor. Being in bed meant taking medicines regularly, lots of reading, 'special' meals and people being considerate.

- Another recalled being off school with flu as a teenager, but sneaking out with her friends to a club in the evening – then being much worse the next day and getting into a lot of trouble with her parents.

- One described a recent experience of being very busy at work, but coughing and sneezing so much that everyone persuaded her to go home. She felt bad sitting about the house, though, not being 'really ill' and knowing her colleagues were working extra hard to cover for her.

- A working mother said that she was too busy to be ill and that if she felt bad she just took a couple of paracetamol tablets and carried on.

For all of us, our sense of well-being fluctuates. One day you may feel particularly well, while on another you feel 'under the weather'. But just feeling a bit down doesn't mean that you are 'ill'. As you can see from the stories above, being 'ill' is associated with the idea that you need to take a break, rest, take medicines or get expert advice. Being ill is *partly* a matter of your body giving signals that things are not right – high temperature, spots, headache, coughing, pain, or tiredness. But it is *also* about putting your normal life on hold.

Being ill means not being in your '*normal*' state of '*health*' (whatever that may be). This has two aspects:

1 not *feeling* normal

2 not being able to *act* as normal.

The first aspect is *biological* – your body doesn't seem right. The other aspect is *social* – you stop carrying on with your normal life. We look more closely now at this social side of illness.

1.2 The sick role

Being ill affects not only you, but also people around you. It changes how they view you and how they relate to you. To tell people that you are 'ill' is to claim a special status. You are saying, 'I need to be treated differently from normal. I need to be excused from some, or all, of my usual duties and be shown sympathy.' You are claiming what is called the 'sick role'.

The sick role

The 'sick role' is a concept introduced by the eminent American sociologist Talcott Parsons (1951, pp. 436–7). Three key features of his account are outlined by present-day sociologist Chris Shilling:

> First, a state of illness is not regarded as the sick person's fault, the individual is 'exempted from responsibility' for their condition, yet has a moral responsibility to regard being sick as undesirable, as something that should be overcome as soon as possible …

> Second, the ill individual is temporarily exempt from 'ordinary daily obligations and expectations'; an exoneration that is not only a right but an obligation … it is not uncommon for people to resist admitting they are sick and for others to legitimize to them their condition by telling them they ought to be at home in bed.

> Third, the sick role incorporates the expectation 'of seeking help' from an appropriate, 'technically competent' health professional and co-operating with them in the process of recovering and returning to full social functioning.

(Source: Shilling, 2002, p. 624)

In other words, when people accept that you are sick they grant you certain privileges, but you also have obligations:

• You are not blamed for being ill, but you are expected to want to get better quickly.

• You are let off your normal duties, but you are also expected to stop doing other things that you normally do.

• You are expected to seek medical advice and to follow it.

A malingerer is someone who shirks their duties by pretending to be ill.

If you seem to be enjoying being ill and to be taking your time over getting better, people will begin to attach blame to your claim of illness. They will begin to think of you as a 'malingerer'. If you are seen out shopping, people question whether you are *really* ill. If you don't rest and take your medicine, people stop sympathising. You are expected to play the sick role properly in order to deserve the privileges it brings. Other people will only play *their* roles in support of your sickness if you play *your* role convincingly.

Activity 2   Applying the 'sick role' concept

Allow about 10 minutes

Go back to your notes from Activity 1 and pick one of your examples of when you were ill. Make notes about whether you think the three features of the sick role (the three bullet points in the paragraph above) apply to your example.

Then do the same for your other examples.

Comment

Here are some thoughts about the four cases in the Comment for Activity 1.

- The mother used her thermometer as a test of whether her son could legitimately claim the sick role. If the temperature reading was high then he was excused school – but only to stay in bed, not to carry on normal games around the house. If the illness persisted, the doctor would be consulted and any treatment prescribed would be strictly adhered to. In other words, the son was dragooned into playing the sick role very correctly.

Playing the sick role

- The teenager with flu had claimed the sick role to the extent of missing school. But then she broke the corresponding expectation that she would cut out leisure pursuits as well. Next day, even though she was feeling more ill, she had forfeited her claim to sympathy by not having played the sick role properly. Instead, she drew strong criticism from her parents.
- The worker with a cold had the sick role pressed upon her by colleagues. But she then felt that she didn't really have a valid claim to it and she felt guilty about not fulfilling her duties.
- The working mother seemed to be saying that she was never in a position to claim the sick role, however ill she might feel.

She had the sick role pressed upon her

Although being ill is to do with something being wrong with your *body*, it is also about playing a *role* and about *moral obligations* to claim the role only when justified and to play it properly, according to expectations.

When claiming the sick role is difficult

Claiming the sick role is relatively simple if you are vomiting or have a broken leg, but some forms of ill health do not present such obvious signs. This can create difficulties in making claims to the sick role. The following extract from a research study illustrates why.

Chronic back pain sufferers: striving for the sick role

The paper [from which this quotation is taken] draws on data from a Norwegian online discussion … for back pain sufferers and from … in-depth interviews with Norwegian back pain sufferers. In both sources, back pain sufferers express a fear that the reality of their pain is being questioned … experiences of delegitimation … [follow from] back pain sufferers' inability to achieve the sick role … A lack of proof that they are sick, including a lack of medical diagnosis, appropriate health care treatment, and visible disabilities, can lead to accusations, both felt and enacted, of malingering, hypochondria and/or mental illness. This in turn can lead to problems in the achievement and/or legitimisation of sick role benefits such as sick leave and medication.

[…]

Individuals who experience bodily suffering but who fail to gain acceptance for this suffering find themselves with illness but without sickness …

(Source: Glenton, 2003, pp. 2243–4)

Learning skills: Should you look up unfamiliar words in a dictionary?

As you were reading the box above, what did you think when you came to the word 'delegitimation'? Were you confident about what it meant? If not, did you wonder whether to look it up in a dictionary? Or did you decide you could guess the meaning well enough? It can be a tricky decision. You don't want to slow down your reading too much. But if you are worried that you don't quite follow the sense of what is being said, then looking something up can save you wasting time getting wrong ideas into your head. In the case above you can probably guess enough to carry on making sense of the text in the box, without looking delegitimation up.

Incidentally, something is 'legitimate' if it is allowed. If someone feels 'legitimated' it means that they feel something has justified them in being where they are and doing what they're doing. Delegitimation is the opposite.

Claire Glenton's paper presents accounts of the experiences of people with long-term back pain whose lives have become a misery. They feel that they are forced to choose between trying to get on with normal life and pretending that they do not feel the pain, or else taking periods of sick leave and risking getting a reputation for malingering. As one wrote online, 'Who hasn't heard them say … "Oh yes, she can paint (or mow the lawn, hang up the clothes) so she can't be that ill!"' (quoted in Glenton, 2003, p. 2248).

Back pain can seem to be a condition that other people don't believe in. One person suggested that when the condition worsened, things could seem better: 'I have to use crutches now, which actually makes it easier to go out … [but] [i]f you go for a walk on a day when you feel good it can … arouse suspicion' (quoted in Glenton, 2003, p. 2248). Others said a spell in hospital could be a relief, because the sick role is taken for granted. In a similar vein, someone in an American back pain study was *glad* to have had three unsuccessful operations because they 'created icons of his travail, scars that he can show people, that he can touch himself to assure himself that there is something "physically wrong" with his back' (Kleinman, quoted in Glenton, 2003, p. 2250).

Back pain – a condition other people don't believe in?

Long-term back pain is bad enough in itself – causing suffering, sleep loss and restricted work and leisure activity – but the impact of the physical condition is made worse by its invisibility, by difficulties in getting a specific diagnosis and by lack of effective treatment regimes (which would demonstrate that you are actively trying to get better). Worse still, being suspected of malingering can lead to psychological problems: depression, loss of self-esteem and feelings of isolation as people hide everyday activities from accusing eyes. And these psychological reactions may cause yet more problems: 'I certainly don't dare tell them that I'm having a hard time psychologically now. Then I'll be diagnosed with mental problems instead of back problems' (quoted in Glenton, 2003, p. 2247).

As you see, a lot can hang on the sick role and your ability to claim it when you need to. Being ill changes your relationship to the world around you. In order to manage the experience of physical illness and be able to draw on appropriate sympathy and support, you have to make a credible claim to the sick role and then act it out according to the rules.

But first, of course, you must recognise the signs of illness and acknowledge to yourself that you are ill. It is to this that we now turn.

1.3 Recognising illness

In this unit you follow the case of Anwar Malik as he experiences various health care services. As with Ann and Angus in Unit 1, this is a fictional case, but based on real life. Here is the first instalment.

Anwar Malik begins to feel unwell

Anwar Malik is a 54-year-old grocer, who lives with his wife Hansa and youngest son Iqbal in a Midlands town. He migrated from Pakistan as a young man. He is Muslim and his first languages are Punjabi and Urdu, but he and his wife speak English in the shop. Their four children were born in the UK. Three now live in nearby towns and visit frequently.

For a while Anwar had been feeling less well than he used to. He felt increasingly tired and lethargic, and was always thirsty. Hansa noticed him being much less active around the house and going to the toilet a lot. Anwar worked a small allotment, growing vegetables for the family, but his previously daily visits dwindled to once a week and he got less and less done when he was there. Hansa became increasingly concerned and urged Anwar to go to the doctor, but he kept saying that she was overreacting – forgetting that he is no longer a young man.

Activity 3   Why do Anwar and Hansa Malik disagree about whether he is ill?

Allow about 10 minutes

Hansa Malik thinks Anwar is ill, but he says he is just slowing down with age. Why would they disagree about this?

Write down what you think their thoughts might be.

(a) What might Hansa Malik's concerns be?

(b) What might Anwar Malik's concerns be?

Comment

Here are my suggestions.

(a) I imagine Hansa being upset to see her husband's health deteriorating and being worried that he might have a condition which requires medical intervention if he is not to become seriously ill. I imagine her wanting to be allowed to help him, but he won't let her.

(b) I imagine Anwar thinking of himself as the man of the house – healthy, vigorous and working hard to provide for his family. Perhaps he thinks of illness as a state of mind that he can ward off by just getting on with life. Maybe he is philosophical about getting older, thinking it important to be able to accept 'slowing down', without getting anxious about it. Perhaps, as an immigrant to the UK, he likes to feel self-sufficient and not a 'burden' on the health services.

Or perhaps he is secretly worried about what a doctor might tell him – unconsciously recognising that he may be ill, but not wanting to let himself think about it.

Perhaps he is resistant to taking on the 'sick role' – not wanting to be 'looked after', to be 'managed' by others – and to stop doing what he normally does.

You probably thought of other things.

People react differently to the physical signs given by bodies. One person may see illness, where another person sees nothing to worry about. Such differences in perceptions can arise for a variety of reasons. They may reflect differences in *temperament* – some people are more anxious than others, or more resistant to taking advice. Or they may reflect differences in *beliefs* – about how the body works, or the nature of illness, or the effectiveness of doctors and medical treatments.

How people react to possible signs of illness is also influenced by their sense of the impact that being ill might have on them – deep *fears*, perhaps, of long-term decline, or of pain and suffering. I have suggested too that Anwar Malik may feel that a serious illness would undermine his *sense of himself* as a strong self-sufficient person, not in need of support from the state or anyone else – and weaken his *identity* as head of the family. Acknowledging significant illness is not a routine thing. It takes time to come to terms with the implications. As you saw with Angus in Unit 1, there can be a long period of denial, allowing you to carry on as you are as long as possible, instead of changing the assumptions by which you live.

Illness, then, is not a simple matter of physical symptoms. It is psychological as well as biological. But in Section 1.1 we also saw that illness is social (because it involves playing the sick role). So illness has to do with people's bodies *and* their minds *and* their social surroundings. To put it another way, being ill has *biological* and *psychological* and *social* aspects. To understand people's health care needs, we have to be aware of all these aspects.

Now we return to Anwar Malik's story.

Anwar gets his eyes tested

Anwar noticed his eyesight getting worse and decided to get some stronger glasses. However, when the optometrist at the chemist's tested his eyes, he said there were worrying signs of degeneration and that he should visit his doctor urgently. Anwar said he'd be fine with some stronger glasses, but the optometrist insisted that he needed some tests to check what was causing the deterioration. He wrote him a note to take to his doctor. Anwar was reluctant. He hadn't been to a doctor for years. However, Hansa argued vehemently that he must go, and Iqbal joined in. As Anwar wavered, Iqbal phoned the GP surgery for an appointment, and finally Anwar consented.

Activity 4   Triggering action

Allow about 5 minutes

What do you think influenced Anwar to change his mind?

Comment

I thought it might be a combination of worry about the prospect of deteriorating eyesight and respect for the optometrist, together with Hansa's seizing of the opportunity:

- to focus attention on the extent of Anwar's deterioration
- to bring Iqbal into her long-running dialogue with Anwar about his health.

So finally, Anwar felt unable to preserve his position as the sensible rationalist, resisting the unnecessary fussing of his wife. At last he acknowledged the possibility that he was ill.

Being ill can carry many personal consequences, so, as suggested above, accepting illness may take time. It involves coming to terms with claiming the 'sick role' and accepting its obligations. All this requires a process of psychological adjustment.

Key points

- We tend to think of illness as something wrong with a person's body.
- However, illness also has social and moral aspects, because it affects how you play your part in life around you. To deserve the 'privileges' of being ill, you are expected to fulfil the obligations of the sick role.
- Illness has a psychological aspect too. People 'read' their bodies' signals differently and react to them differently.
- Recognising illness involves coming to terms with the personal consequences of taking on the sick role.

Learning skills: A suitable environment for learning

Now that you are into your second unit of K101, where are you doing this reading? Is it the right place to get the best out of yourself? You're going to be spending quite a lot of time studying in the months ahead, so it's worth pausing to think about whether you have set yourself up with as good a learning environment as you can. For ideas on this have a quick look through Section 2.4 of *The Good Study Guide* (pages 40–4).

Reader

2 Health care in the community

Anwar Malik's consultation with the optometrist was a first step out of the private family world of informal care into the public sphere of professional health care services. Now his decision to see his doctor connects him with his local community health services.

2.1 Accessing primary care

Specifically, Anwar has decided to make use of a *primary care* service, his local GP.

Activity 5   Knowing your primary care services

Allow about 5 minutes

You have almost certainly used primary care services – but why are they called primary?

What does a GP do and what does the term 'general practitioner' mean?

Just jot down what you think. It's an opportunity to check what you already know. If you can't answer – look below.

Comment

This is what the NHS Direct website says about primary care.

Primary care

Healthcare in the UK is divided into 'primary' and 'secondary' services.

Primary care services are provided by the people you normally see when you first have a health problem. It might be a visit to a doctor or dentist, to an optician for an eye test, or a trip to a pharmacist to buy cough mixture. NHS Walk-in Centres and the NHS Direct phone service are also part of primary care.

(Source: NHS Direct, 2007c)

The following description of the role of a general practitioner (or GP) is taken from the Medical Schools & Nursing Colleges Worldwide website.

General practitioner

The general practitioner is the first point of contact for most medical services. The bulk of the work is carried out during consultations in the surgery and during home visits …

General Practitioners provide a complete spectrum of care within the local community: dealing with problems that often combine physical, psychological and social components …

[…]

General Practitioners call on an extensive knowledge of medical conditions to be able to assess a problem and decide on the appropriate course of action. They know how and when to intervene, through treatment, prevention and education, to promote the health of their patients and families.

(Source: Medical Schools & Nursing Colleges Worldwide, 2007)

Primary health care services, then, are those which are directly accessible to you. In other words, you make your own decision to use them. Secondary services are available to you through being 'referred' (i.e. sent on) from a primary service – for example, to a renal unit in a hospital.

And we see that a GP (general practitioner) is a medical doctor who works in the community, providing primary care. A 'practitioner' is someone who is qualified to 'practise' a profession. About half of medical practitioners specialise in a particular branch of medicine; for example, cardiology or dermatology. But about half don't specialise, choosing instead to be *general* practitioners – otherwise known as GPs, or family doctors, or community doctors.

The word 'practice' is used to mean the place you go to see your GP, as in:

> Your local doctors' surgery or GP practice provides a wide range of family health services …

(NHS Choices, 2007)

Since a GP is a 'first point of contact' with the health services, Anwar Malik made an appropriate decision in arranging to see his local GP. He could also have gone to a local NHS Walk-in Centre, or telephoned NHS Direct for advice (or NHS24 if he had lived in Scotland).

2.2 Entering the medical world

A visit to a doctor can be an unnerving experience for someone who isn't used to it.

Consulting the doctor

Arriving at Hilltop Surgery, Anwar felt awkward – unsure whom to speak to, or what to say. A woman behind a counter asked if she could help. Then she asked him some questions and typed on a keyboard. He handed her the optometrist's note and started to explain what was wrong with him, but she asked him to sit in the waiting room. He sat worrying what to say to the doctor – afraid it might all sound trivial and that the doctor might not understand his English properly. As people's names were called, he wondered if he'd been forgotten. But eventually he heard his name and was directed to a room.

Dr Emma Rees welcomed him and asked some general questions, then detailed ones about his eyesight, tiredness, thirst, and so on. Then she examined him physically. At times Anwar started to explain what he thought was going on with his health and his life generally, but Dr Rees continued to pursue her investigations. Then she said she wanted to check some possibilities and asked Anwar to see Practice Nurse Jacinta Kapelski. Nurse Kapelski gave him a bottle and asked him to pop into the toilet to provide a sample of urine. This made him feel uncomfortable. He wasn't used to talking with a woman about such things. Nurse Kapelski tested the sample, checked his blood pressure, and asked him about his eating habits. She found high levels of glucose in his urine and followed up with a blood test which indicated the same. Then she explained to Anwar that he might have diabetes, but that more tests were needed. She gave him a form and asked him to visit the outpatient department at the local hospital the next morning and not to eat anything before the visit.

Activity 6   Being at the doctor's

Allow about 10 minutes

(a) How do you think Anwar was feeling during this visit to the doctor – and why?

(b) Do you think his feelings would make any difference to the benefits he gets from his visit?

Waiting to see a GP

Comment

(a) It's clear that the doctor's surgery was an unfamiliar environment for Anwar, in terms both of the physical surroundings – the reception counter, waiting room, etc. – and of the atmosphere, the formal, busy way in which staff related to him, and the general silence in the waiting room. There was little chance of conversation or getting to know people. Everybody was pleasant, but all kept their distance. It's easy to feel 'different' in an environment where people don't 'chat' with you – to feel that they all belong there, while you don't. Anwar also felt uncomfortable about the way private things, such as going to the toilet, were talked about openly, even by members of the opposite sex. Anwar wanted to explain himself – why he was there, what had been happening in his life – but there wasn't a chance to do much more than answer questions. I imagine him wondering whether his condition has been properly understood, particularly as English is not his first language.

(b) As he was already feeling anxious, I imagine him finding it hard to concentrate on what people said, and hard to take in the implications.

Staff at a doctor's surgery are busy. They cannot have lengthy conversations with everyone. They are required to follow established procedures and maintain accurate records – and they are expected to provide the same standard of service to everyone, all of which can create a certain amount of formality. However, this rather odd environment feels 'normal' to staff, so it may be hard for them to see how unsettling it can be for someone who visits infrequently. Misunderstandings can easily arise. For example, Anwar's eagerness to explain his experiences might be interpreted as an attempt to get special attention, or as lack of cooperation with those trying to help him.

A doctor's surgery has its own culture – taken for granted by staff, but potentially disconcerting for people not used to attending. Yet care services rely on good communications between staff and those seeking the services. Communications work best when people feel reasonably relaxed and confident that there will be time to sort out confusions. So, health care staff need to be aware that what is their routine work environment may create significant communication barriers for others.

Getting the test results

Anwar went to the hospital, where blood samples were taken. He was told that the results would be sent to his GP and a week later he received a phone call from Hilltop Surgery asking him to visit. Dr Rees told Anwar that the tests showed he had Type 2 diabetes. She explained that this is a chronic disease which requires regular self-testing, medication, exercise and a change to his diet – otherwise serious complications might follow, including further damage to his eyesight, or to his heart, kidneys or limbs. Dr Rees prescribed tablets and asked Anwar to see Nurse Kapelski again. She checked his blood sugar and wrote the results in his records. Then she made him appointments at the diabetes clinic attached to the surgery, to see the diabetes specialist nurse and the community dietician. Anwar went home worried, confused and in a state of shock.

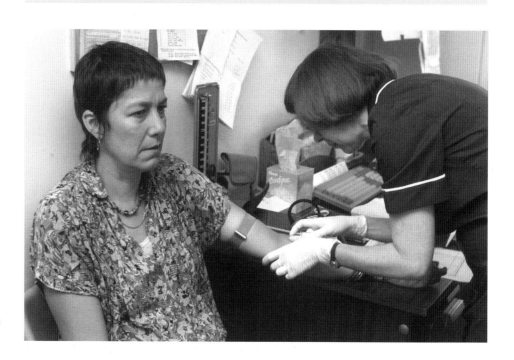

A practice nurse carries out health checks

2.3 Coming to terms with a chronic condition

A visit to a doctor may bring news that is hard to come to terms with.

Activity 7   The experience of finding out about a chronic disease
Allow about 10 minutes

(a) What is a chronic disease? Write down what you think.

(b) Write down some reasons why Anwar is worried, confused and in a state of shock.

Comment

(a) A disease is an abnormality of body or mind. A chronic disease is one that is long-lasting or recurring.

(b) Possible reasons for Anwar's reactions:

Worried	He has been told that unless he follows a treatment programme he could experience worsening eyesight and damage to other parts of his body.
Confused	What is diabetes? How does it affect you? What will he need to do?
In shock	It is only a week since Anwar first accepted that he might be ill – now he has learned that he has a condition requiring daily treatment and a special diet for the rest of his life.

For Dr Rees and Nurse Kapelski a disease such as diabetes is part of daily working life, but for Anwar the news is likely to be shocking, however sensitively things are discussed. If he is to participate successfully in keeping the condition under control, the health care professionals he meets will need to take account of the emotional and practical stresses he experiences and provide continuing support.

DVD

Activity 8   Understanding diabetes
Allow about 15 minutes

As you follow the case of Anwar Malik, it will help to know something about diabetes.

Listen now to Professor David Matthews, a leading expert on diabetes, explaining what it is and how it is treated.

Put the DVD in your computer and find Block 1, Unit 2, Activity 8. Then work your way through the activity.

Comment

You now have an overview of Anwar's condition. Essentially, his blood sugar level keeps rising too high because his body is not making enough insulin. To keep himself feeling well and to avoid further damage to his eyes and other parts of his body, he needs to keep checking his blood sugar level and taking action to keep it within bounds.

Note that this information about diabetes is to give you a general idea of the nature of the disease and its implications. *You don't need to memorise the details.* This is a course about 'care', not about 'biology' or 'medicine'.

You could quickly find out more about diabetes by going to the NHS Direct website, www.nhsdirect.nhs.uk (or to Scotland's NHS24 website, www.nhs24.com) and typing 'diabetes' in the search box. For example, it provides information about how common diabetes is:

> Diabetes affects 2 million people in the UK and there may be as many as a million more people who have the condition but do not know about it. ... Nine out of ten people with diabetes have type 2 diabetes and over 80% of these people are overweight.

(NHS Direct, 2007b)

This means that over 2% of the population are known to have diabetes, with perhaps another 1.5% undiagnosed. These figures are rising, making diabetes a key target for national health campaigns.

If you are affected by diabetes yourself, you will obviously come across much in this unit that is familiar. Some of the situations described may be similar to ones you have experienced. Others may be contrary to your experience. Either way, your expertise in diabetes will enrich your learning as you study the unit.

2.4 The community health care network

Learning to manage the condition

At the Hilltop diabetes clinic, Diabetes Specialist Nurse Elston Richards showed Anwar how to use a kit for self-monitoring of blood glucose. Then he talked to him about how to manage his condition and gave him some leaflets. He advised him to test his glucose level regularly and take his tablets at the same times every day. He recommended carrying glucose or sweets whenever he went out, in case he became unwell. He also explained the importance of his diet and regular exercise. Then Anwar saw Erin Kennedy, the community dietician, who recommended a special diet and gave him some diet advice sheets.

Anwar Malik has now met five people at the doctor's surgery – receptionist, GP, practice nurse, diabetes specialist nurse and community dietician – quite apart from those he met when he went to the hospital for tests. This gives a glimpse of how intricate the system of community health care is. Years ago, many GPs practised more or less independently, often with minimal support:

> In the 1950s three surveys showed that the average practice was made up of one or two GPs. Around 50% had some form of administrative support in the shape of a secretary or receptionist, in many cases the GP's spouse. Less than 50% of practices employed a practice nurse.
>
> … many GPs practised from their own homes …
>
> (Royal College of General Practitioners, 2003, p. 2)

Now most GPs practise as members of primary health care teams (PHCTs). A PHCT will usually be managed by a practice manager and include several GPs, as well as a variety of other health professionals and administrative staff. For example, the website of the Danescourt Surgery in Cardiff shows that it has a PHCT of twenty, consisting of five doctors, a practice nurse, four district nurses, a midwife, a health visitor, a practice manager and seven reception and administrative staff (Danescourt Surgery, 2007). This means that anyone using the practice can access a wide range of coordinated health care services.

By contacting his GP, Anwar has connected himself with a system of support at Hilltop Surgery. Staff there can also put him in touch with other support networks in his area, or he could search online. For example, the website in the illustration below shows the wide range of support available to people with diabetes in the Tayside region of Scotland (Tayside Diabetes Network: www.diabetes-healthnet.ac.uk).

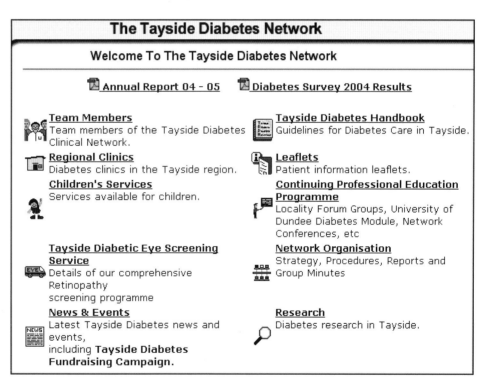

Website of the NHS Tayside Diabetes Managed Clinical Network

As well as support from health professionals, there are volunteer support groups and self help groups. Anwar could visit the Diabetes UK website (www.diabetes.org.uk), enter his postcode and find a local support group. The website also provides a lot of information about diabetes and about current initiatives and developments.

Website of Diabetes UK

The situation for someone seeking support for a long-term condition has changed dramatically in the past fifty years. Instead of relying on advice from a GP practising, perhaps, from his own home, with his wife as receptionist, people can now take advantage of local and national networks offering a wide range of expertise and support.

Key points

- The term 'primary care' refers to all the health services which people can access directly, without being referred.
- Most primary care is provided through primary health care teams, made up of GPs and a variety of other health care professionals, plus administrative staff.
- A visit to a GP provides a first point of contact with the health services.
- The medical world has its own distinctive culture, which is different from most people's everyday lives, so a doctor's surgery can be an unsettling environment.
- A condition such as diabetes has lifelong consequences for the person who has it, and requires a major commitment to participation in self-care.
- For common chronic diseases there are usually networks of support within the community.

3 Being aware of the service user

There may be complex networks of health care services in the community, but this does not guarantee that they meet the needs of 'service users'.

The term 'service user'

When talking about care, it is not easy to find a general term for the person receiving care. In a hospital the term 'patient' is used, but it has a flavour of the impersonal, of passivity, and it doesn't really fit 'social care' situations. 'Client' sounds rather formal and 'posh' for some caring situations, while 'customer' sounds too commercial. In the end, the term 'service user' has become widely adopted. It isn't particularly elegant, but at least it emphasises the idea of a 'service', rather than things being 'done' to you, and also the idea of being active – of 'making your own use of' – rather than just passively 'receiving'.

Me – a service user?

Now we follow Anwar Malik's experiences as a service user.

Disappointing progress

Anwar attended the Hilltop diabetes clinic for several weeks, but his blood glucose levels did not stay stable. Diabetes Specialist Nurse Elston Richards asked him if he was taking his tablets, sticking to his diet and taking regular exercise, and Anwar nodded. But when Nurse Richards asked more questions, it became clear that Anwar wasn't taking all the tablets he was prescribed, or following the diet and the exercise programme very closely.

Activity 9 Why not stick to the treatment?

Allow about 5 minutes

Why would Anwar not stick closely to a recommended treatment programme? Is he being irresponsible or lazy? Is he not paying enough attention to what he's told? Or might there be other reasons which make sticking to the programme difficult for Anwar?

Write down any reasons you can think of as to why someone might not stick exactly to their doctor's recommendations.

Comment

Below are some reasons given by Anwar himself.

Difficulties experienced by Anwar and Hansa

Anwar Malik told Nurse Richards that he found it hard to follow the diet and exercise guidelines, because they didn't fit in with his culture. Also, Hansa didn't read English so she hadn't been able to use the meal planning leaflet given to them. However, he had relatives with diabetes who were giving him advice. As Anwar talked, Nurse Richards noticed that he seemed confused about glucose and insulin in his blood and how the tablets and diet were supposed to affect them. He realised that Anwar needed more help with understanding both diabetes and the treatment.

3.1 Culturally appropriate services

Why did Anwar struggle with the diabetes diet? Table 1 shows one of the diet sheets he was given. You do not need to look too hard for clues.

Table 1 The diabetes diet recommended to Anwar Malik

Morning Breakfast	Afternoon Lunch	Evening Supper	Night Nightcap
Cereal (1 portion of cornflakes, or 2 Weetabix) and/or slice of toast with spread and sugar-free conserves	1 portion of carbohydrate (potatoes or pasta)	1 portion of carbohydrate (potatoes or pasta)	Milky drink: tea/ Horlicks/coffee
	2 portions of vegetables	2 portions of vegetables	Cream crackers or fruit
Tea with milk, no sugar	1 portion of meat or fish	1 portion of meat or fish	
Mid-morning	Fresh fruit for dessert	Fresh fruit or sugar-free dessert	
Tea/coffee	Tea/coffee with milk, no sugar	Water, fruit juice or tea/ coffee with milk	
Cream crackers or fruit			

It is easy to see why Anwar and Hansa might find this diet hard to follow, with its exclusive focus on Western foods and eating patterns. But what about other aspects of Anwar's treatment programme? Do they also present cultural difficulties?

Activity 10   Cultural barriers to maintaining a treatment programme
Allow about 45 minutes

This is quite a long activity, but very useful. It involves reading the findings of a research report on the experiences of Scottish South Asians with diabetes.

First draw a bigger version of the table below on a sheet of A4 paper, making it fill the page.

	Reasons for not sticking to regime	**How to improve support**
Diet		
Tablets		
Exercise		

Resources

Then find Resource 2, 'Pakistani and Indian patients' experiences of Scottish diabetes services: a qualitative study', by Julia Lawton and her associates in the Resources.

Go to the heading 'Key findings' (page 00) and read from there to the end of the chapter, highlighting any points that seem relevant to Anwar Malik's experience. (If you don't have a highlighter pen, just underline.) Look for anything that helps in understanding why Anwar did not stick to his recommended regime of tablets, diet and exercise. Also highlight any ideas which might help in supporting Anwar better.

Then go back through your highlighting and make notes in your table.

Finally, make a note of why this study was undertaken.

Comment

The study was carried out because South Asian residents of the UK are over four times as likely to be affected by diabetes than the rest of the population. As 2% of the general population have diabetes (see Section 2.3, above), that means more than 8% of the South Asian population are affected – or about one in twelve.

Here is how my table turned out. (Don't worry if yours looks different.)

	Reasons for not sticking to regime	**How to improve support**
Diet	Diet changes tend to be remedial (i.e. only when feeling ill)	More explanation as to how diet works and why it's so important
	Traditional food is central to identity	Culturally appropriate diet advice
	Can't refuse hospitality	Visual and oral aids for those who don't read
	Family eats together	Support with adjusting to lifestyle changes
	Wife responsible for food	Discuss cooking methods
	Confusion about diets	Discuss diet with whole family
	Culturally inappropriate diets	
	Resistance to Western diet foods	
Tablets	Poor diabetes knowledge	Appropriately targeted, culturally sensitive diabetes services
	Language difficulty makes asking questions awkward	Allow extra time for language difficulties, especially when interpreters are involved
Exercise	Working long, antisocial hours	Realistic, culturally appropriate advice
	Exercising not part of culture, so makes you stand out	Targets negotiated with the service user
	Limited cultural sport activity	

The Khush Dil project in Edinburgh runs cookery workshops to help reduce diabetes and heart disease

This research shows that someone from a South Asian background may experience many challenges in trying to follow a diabetes treatment regime. In falling short with his programme, Anwar is no different from many others.

Also, in not having a very clear understanding of the nature of diabetes and the way his medication is meant to work, Anwar may be influenced by beliefs and values within his community. In another paper based on the same research study, the researchers report that:

> Many … believed that drugs … worked by providing instant relief of symptoms. Hence they often saw it as unnecessary to take all of their [tablets] when they felt well: 'You just can't be bothered taking them for the sake of it' (… Pakistani, female).
>
> […]
>
> [Some had a] perception that … being more potent … than medicines available on the Indian subcontinent, [their tablets] could have hazardous effects. … that, if taken in excess or over long periods, [their tablets] could be detrimental to their health:
>
> > 'Yes, they told me to take it everyday, but I said "do I want to die by taking it everyday … I don't want to die by taking so many."'
>
> (… Pakistani, female)
>
> (Lawton et al., 2005, p. 1248)

It is easy to understand why people want to make choices for themselves about when and what to eat and when to take medicines. Nobody wants to spend a lifetime following strict rules. However, people with diabetes need to be well enough informed to make appropriate choices. Anwar needs to understand the nature of the disease and how the treatment works if he is to manage his treatment programme effectively within his cultural environment. The more he can become an 'expert patient', the better he will be able to adapt his recommended regime to fit his own life. Providing him with information was a first step, but opportunities for education in diabetes and for discussion of cultural factors will help him to take control of his treatment programme.

DVD

Activity 11   Sensitivity to cultural differences

Allow about 6 minutes

David Matthews is well aware of the importance of people's cultural environment in successful management of diabetes. Listen as he illustrates vividly why cultural sensitivity is important.

Go to the DVD and find Block 1, Unit 2, Activity 11.

Comment

As David Matthews makes clear, every patient's cultural context presents challenges, but also offers opportunities. He regards it as essential to be aware of cultural differences and to take them into account in advising his patients.

Making Anwar's programme culturally sensitive

At a team meeting at Hilltop Surgery, Diabetes Specialist Nurse Richards discussed with Dr Rees, Practice Nurse Kapelski and Community Dietician Kennedy how to modify Anwar Malik's treatment programme to make it more compatible with his culture and lifestyle. Dietician Kennedy said that she would meet with Hansa and Anwar to work out a more appropriate diet plan with them, and that she would provide pictorial guidelines for Hansa. Nurse Richards said he would discuss with both of them how they could manage family and social life to support Anwar's diet. He also said he would contact a South Asian diabetes support group, to help support Anwar and Hansa in understanding the implications of the disease and the treatment.

But are cultural factors the only reason why Anwar struggled with his treatment programme?

3.2 Psychologically sensitive services

Further developments

In spite of Anwar's and Hansa's efforts, and those of the Hilltop team, Anwar's condition worsened over the following months. Eventually Dr Rees decided that he should start on insulin injections, so she discussed this with Anwar. Then Nurse Kapelski showed him how to inject himself. He seemed to adapt to this quite well, but after a couple of months his attendance at the diabetes clinics declined. And when Anwar *did* attend, Nurse Richards felt that he was not as communicative as before. It became hard to get a sense of how things were going, but he suspected they weren't going well.

Activity 12   Morale and diabetes regimes

Allow about 30 minutes

In spite of the Hilltop primary health care team's efforts to make Anwar's treatment programme more culturally appropriate, things seem not to be going well.

(a) Can you think of any reasons why that might be? Jot down your ideas.

(b) Do you think Anwar is refusing to cooperate? Should he be described as 'non-compliant'?

(c) What should Nurse Richards do? Write down any suggestions.

Resources

Then find Resource 3, 'Encouraging effective self-management in diabetes', by William Polonsky in the Resources. Read the article, highlighting any points that seem relevant to Anwar's case.

Working from your highlighting, make a list of some of the issues that might affect Anwar.

Comment

(a) Here are some of Polonsky's suggestions as to why someone in Anwar's position might struggle with his treatment programme:

- Living with diabetes can seem like a demanding job with no holidays.

- He may, like many people with diabetes, suffer from bouts of depression, making it hard to sustain his motivation.

- He may feel overwhelmed by the complications of testing and managing his blood sugar level.

- He may find it hard to keep doing things which show few effects for lots of effort.

- He may feel guilty about his failures in sticking to his treatment programme – thereby exacerbating any depression.

- When he has slipped with his programme, he may be tempted to skip his blood tests too, to avoid evidence of the consequences.

- He may miss sessions at the diabetes clinics because he feels a failure in the 'job' of being a diabetes patient and that he has let down Nurse Richards.

(b) If Anwar isn't keeping on top of all aspects of the 'job', this is unlikely to be deliberate 'non-compliance'. Most likely, he hopes for a long and healthy life but is struggling with personal obstacles.

(c) Here is my list of suggestions for Nurse Richards:

- Try to engage Anwar in a discussion which 'normalises' the struggles of managing diabetes and encourages him to be open about setbacks in his own self-care.

- Discuss realistic self-care goals and targets with him and try to support him in developing a workable plan.

- Talk about the value of regular clinic visits and encourage him to come even when things haven't been going well.

Learning skills: How fast should you read?

Apart from the main Unit 2 text, you are asked to read other pieces such as the Polonsky article above. Being 'ambushed' by these additional readings can throw your time plans out. That is why we put a book symbol in the margin – so as you flick through the pages ahead, you can easily pick out any extra reading. We suggested that you spent 30 minutes on the last activity, of which 25 minutes were intended for the reading. How long did the reading actually take you?

Reader

You need to take notice of how long different kinds of reading take, so that you can adjust your reading speed. To help you think about strategies for getting through the reading ahead of you, take a quick look at Section 5.4.3 of *The Good Study Guide* (pages 115–16).

It is not unusual that Anwar has experienced difficulties in sticking to his prescribed treatment programme. Nor is it unusual when he loses heart and stops attending the clinic. In supporting treatment of chronic conditions, it is important that health care teams take into account a person's own ideas, feelings, hopes and fears, as well as their cultural context.

DVD

Activity 13   Psychological responses to diabetes

Allow about 15 minutes

You have already heard David Matthews' views on the importance of cultural sensitivity in advising diabetes patients. Now you can hear what he thinks about the need for psychological sensitivity.

Go to the DVD and find Block 1, Unit 2, Activity 13.

Comment

David Matthews is quick to emphasise that people vary a lot in their psychological response to diabetes. He also makes clear that 'engaging' with patients and helping them to keep the demands of diabetes programmes in proportion is a vital part of his work.

You may recall that the 'sick role' requires people to seek medical advice and *follow* it. People who fall short of some of the prescriptions of a diabetes regime may feel that they are failing in playing the sick role – and so are to blame for their condition and not deserving of medical services. David Matthews seeks to reassure his patients that no blame is involved and that it is up to them to come to their own compromises with the recommendations and the risks.

Of course, psychological pressures do not arise only from diabetes. Life throws up other sources of stress:

> When my dad died just after that, like I was sitting down thinking and I eat more. I eat more. Thinking about it. Your diabetes you should control yourself but it is hard. I don't like diabetes. And with other things like my father, like him dying, I start thinking and I sit down and I eat more.

(Quoted in Bissell et al., 2004, p. 855)

People's psychological responses to illness and treatment are a significant factor in the success of a treatment programme.

3.3 Taking account of people's lives

You have seen how cultural and psychological challenges can make it hard to stick to a diabetes treatment programme. But there are other aspects of people's lives which have an impact too. In a study of South Asians with diabetes living in the north-west of England, Paul Bissell and his associates found that:

> ... diabetic management imposed additional financial burdens on patients and their families, over and above the costs of everyday living ...

> > Money is the main thing. I don't work, my husband is out of work now, for 6 weeks. When we get money in [from social security] then we have food for the family. After that, we don't, we live on what we have. And I have to eat whatever we have.

> > [Interviewer]. Does that mean that your diet suffers as a result?

> > I eat anything. Yes, I will eat what ... it is ... that we have.

> (Bissell et al., 2004, p. 855)

Low income, then, can be another obstacle to sticking to a diet. Also, the area in which a person lives may not have easy access to shops that sell suitable types of food. In other words, *social* and *economic* circumstances can present further challenges to maintaining a prescribed treatment programme.

So, treating a complicated long-term condition such as diabetes involves a lot more than taking readings of blood sugar levels and prescribing insulin. It is not simply a matter of 'biology' and 'medicine'. It also involves taking account of the person and the life they lead and involving them in the process of managing their condition. Of course, as David Matthews makes clear, biological science and medical science made treatment of diabetes possible.

- *Biological science* discovered the role of insulin and then found ways to obtain supplies of it.

- *Medical science* researched the effects on people of doses of insulin.

But 'biomedicine' on its own is not enough. A diabetes programme is not just a matter of a doctor treating a disease within a body. The whole person has to be included as an active participant in the programme.

Diabetes self-care

The classic 'biomedical' approach to health care is that the doctor *diagnoses* what is physically wrong with the patient, then *prescribes* a treatment. During the processes of diagnosis and prescription the patient is passive – almost like an outsider, watching the expert at work on a body that happens to be theirs. After this the patient follows the doctor's instructions. But both William Polonsky and

David Matthews make clear that this idea of the *passive* patient is inadequate. A patient with diabetes needs to be in *active* dialogue with the doctor and other health care workers, so that they can cooperate intelligently and resourcefully in their treatment programme. Polonsky, in Resource 3, advocates finding 'ways to encourage greater openness during patient interviews', while Matthews, on the DVD, talks of 'a real necessity for health care professionals to be engaging with patients'.

The language of health care has tended to take for granted the idea of the patient who passively follows expert advice. A Royal Pharmaceutical Society (RPS) Working Party pointed out that the use of the term 'non-compliant' to describe patients who do not take prescribed medicines implies that they have a *duty* to comply – whereas it is much better if they collaborate in medication programmes willingly. The RPS has proposed that the term 'compliance' should be replaced by 'concordance':

> The pursuit of 'compliance' has hitherto suggested that the aim of prescribing was to get the patient to 'follow doctor's orders'. There was an unspoken assumption that the patient's role was to be passive and that since the prescriber's view was rational and evidence-based, it was, for these reasons, 'superior' to the beliefs and wishes of the patient. These assumptions are challenged by an alternative model of the consultation which our working party describes as 'concordance'.

> Concordance is based on the notion that the work of prescriber and patient in the consultation is a negotiation between equals and that therefore the aim is a therapeutic alliance between them. This alliance may, in the end, include an agreement to differ. Its strength lies in a new assumption of respect for the patient's agenda and the creation of openness in the relationship, so that both doctor and patient together can proceed on the basis of reality and not of misunderstanding, distrust or concealment.

(Royal Pharmaceutical Society Working Party, 1997, p. 8)

(You could keep a look out for the word 'concordance' and make your own judgement about the success of the RPS Working Party's proposal.)

Consultation as a negotiation between equals

Effective health care involves engaging with, informing, educating and supporting people so that they can participate in managing their own treatment programmes within the circumstances of their lives. This means adopting a *service user perspective*: finding out how people feel about and make sense of their illnesses, engaging them in discussing how to treat their illnesses, and making sure that treatment takes account of people's cultural contexts, social circumstances and lifestyles.

Key points

- To be effective, health care needs to take account of the 'service user perspective'.
- Health care for long-term conditions needs to be attuned to the cultural background of the service user.
- It also needs to take account of the service user's social circumstances; for example, their ability to afford a prescribed programme.
- And it needs to take account of the service user's psychological reactions to illness and to treatment.
- Successful health care for long-term conditions involves more than health care professionals applying biomedical science. It also involves engaging service users as partners in their own care programmes.
- This includes supporting them in becoming 'expert patients' who can take an active part in understanding and managing their own care.

We now return to Anwar Malik as his condition takes a turn for the worse.

Another development

Nurse Richards visited Anwar at home to try to establish a better relationship and help him refocus his treatment programme. After that, Anwar started attending the clinic again.

One time he arrived wearing an open-toe slipper, saying he couldn't get his foot into a shoe as it was swollen. He said he'd bumped his toe a few weeks earlier and had noticed a bruise but had thought nothing of it.

When Nurse Richards examined Anwar's foot, he saw immediately that it looked gangrenous. He told Dr Rees, who looked at the foot and said that Anwar should go straight to hospital to see the diabetes specialist. Anwar didn't want to go, as Hansa couldn't drive the car back home. But Nurse Richards said that Hansa could go with Anwar in the ambulance and that they would make arrangements later about the car.

4 Care in hospitals

'Acute means occurring suddenly or over a short period of time' (NHS Direct, 2007a). In the world of health care, 'acute' means the opposite of 'chronic' or long-term.

Up to this point, Anwar Malik has received treatment for diabetes within the *primary* care services. Now, going to hospital, he is entering *secondary*, or *acute*, care services.

4.1 Why go to hospital?

Why does Anwar need to go to hospital? What kinds of health care services are provided there?

Activity 14   What services do hospitals provide?

Allow about 5 minutes

Why would you go to hospital rather than get health care from your GP? What kinds of health care services would you expect a hospital to provide? Jot down a few thoughts.

Comment

Here is what the NHS Direct website says:

> **What services do hospitals provide?**
>
> Sometimes, a problem cannot be sorted out by primary care. In this case, you may need to go to hospital for further tests or an operation. NHS hospitals have a range of services to treat rare, complicated and serious conditions. You may need to go to hospital for procedures that cannot be carried out in your GP surgery, such as scans, X-rays and surgery.
>
> Hospitals also carry out emergency treatment for serious injuries and life-threatening illnesses. Many hospitals have intensive care units for seriously ill people who need round the clock treatment.
>
> Hospitals have lots of different clinics to treat particular conditions. The number of clinics vary, depending on the size of the hospital, and some hospitals specialise in certain areas of medicine.
>
> (NHS Direct, 2007d)

Broadly speaking, *general* practitioners (GPs) work in surgeries within the community, while *specialist* doctors work in hospitals (although this is changing, as we shall see later). Hospital is a place where you expect to have access to:

- diagnosis and treatment by specialist consultants
- complicated treatments requiring teams of different specialists (e.g. surgeons, anaesthetists, nurses)
- advanced, 'hi-tech' medical equipment
- intensive, round-the-clock nursing care for critical conditions
- specialist nursing care for rare or complicated conditions
- strictly controlled medication, along with close observation of changes in condition.

A hospital is a place where the full powers of modern science can be brought to bear on diagnosing and treating diseases and on supporting patients through critical stages of recovery.

DVD

Activity 15 Science and modern medicine

Allow about 10 minutes

Listen now to David Matthews talking about the scientific approach to studying the human body, and the impact science has had on medical practice.

Go to the DVD and find Block 1, Unit 2, Activity 15.

Comment

As David Matthews explains, the scientific method is based on:

* systematic observations and experiments, recorded in detail and repeated many times.

Applying this scientific approach to medicine led to the development of *biomedical science* which has given us:

* increasingly detailed and reliable models of how the body works, enabling us to understand better how things go wrong

* an ever-expanding range of new treatments along with relatively reliable knowledge of their effects.

The success of biomedicine has transformed Western medical practice.

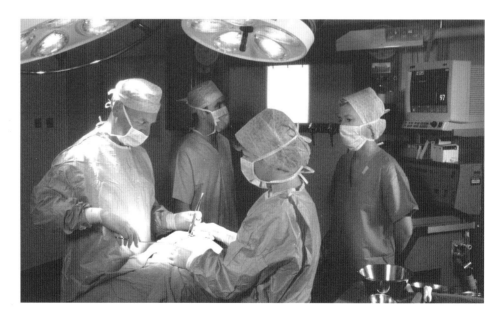

A team of biomedical experts with high-tech equipment

The way health care developed under the influence of biological and medical science has been called the 'biomedical model':

> ... the model of health and disease which came to dominate Western thinking after about 1800 ... was grounded in biology and other sciences. Overriding importance was given to learning about anatomy and physiology, in particular to understanding mechanisms such as the heart, arteries, nerves, brain and so on. The body was conceptualised as

a machine in which all the parts functioned together to ensure health; if some parts broke down, clinicians intervened to limit and treat the damage.

(Jones, 1994, p. 377)

A modern hospital might be thought of as a kind of laboratory of biomedical science, where your body can be scientifically observed and treated; that is an environment:

- designed to enable systematic observation of the biological structures and processes within your body, sometimes using complex scientific equipment such as CT scanners and MRI scanners

- where sophisticated medical interventions can be undertaken, under laboratory-like conditions, by teams of scientifically trained specialists.

However, not all the science is 'hi-tech'. A hospital is also a place where, as you lie in a ward bed:

- your bodily functions can be kept under systematic observation through routine monitoring and recording of temperature, heart rate and blood pressure

- the healing of a wound can be monitored when dressings are changed

- medication can be systematically administered and recorded, while a suitable regime of diet and drink is maintained, unhindered by the routines and habits of your normal life.

Alternatively, you might make periodic day visits to hospital to consult a specialist to track the progress of a long-term condition.

All these, whether or not they involve advanced equipment, are applications of 'science', because they involve systematic observation, systematic interventions and systematic record keeping.

Hospitals serve as the 'headquarters' of biomedical science. Most leading medical scientists are, like David Matthews, based in hospitals. And although a wide variety of non-biomedical activities are carried out in hospitals (e.g. by occupational therapists, social workers, receptionists, cleaners, caterers, technicians, finance officers and administrators), it is the work of the staff trained in biomedicine which tends to take priority in the way the hospital is organised.

4.2 Being a hospital patient

So what is it like to take your body along to hospital to be observed and treated by biomedical science – staying in an environment where your bodily processes are the main focus of concern, rather than you as a person?

Emergency admittance

Anwar was taken from the ambulance to lie on a trolley in a corridor, while a bed was prepared. Hansa sat alongside, very upset. A receptionist came and took details. After a while, Anwar was wheeled to a ward bed. Ward Nurse Grace Taylor pulled curtains round and asked Anwar to undress to his underwear and put on a robe which tied at the back, while she stepped outside. Then she asked him to lie down, examined his foot and made notes. An hour later, Rajat Gupta, registrar in diabetes and endocrinology, came to examine Anwar. He confirmed that gangrene was spreading upwards from his foot. He said he was afraid that it would be necessary to amputate below his knee. Anwar and Hansa were stunned. Half an hour later, surgeon Gavin MacLaren arrived, examined Anwar's leg and confirmed that amputation was urgently required. The operation was booked for the following morning. Health care assistant Millie Harrison brought some pyjamas for Anwar. Then anaesthetist Zoe Greenroyd came to ask Anwar to sign some consent forms which, after a despairing discussion with Hansa, he did. A miserable hour later, there seemed nothing more to say, so Hansa went home, leaving Anwar in a state of agitation. How could this be happening? When Millie, the health care assistant, asked if he wanted anything, Anwar was bad tempered. Although there were other people in the ward, he didn't want to talk to them. He felt very alone and helpless.

Sadly, the decision to amputate Anwar's lower leg is not uncommon. This is one of the recognised 'complications' associated with diabetes:

> In the UK every year 5,000 people with diabetes have an amputation – that's 100 people every week. More than one in ten foot ulcers result in an amputation …

> (NHS National Diabetes Support Team, 2006, p. 1)

Amputation is a common event for the doctors and nurses, but for Anwar it is a devastating development. His life is about to change and all he can do is lie there, feeling cast adrift from everything important in his life.

Anwar has entered the role of 'hospital patient'. This is an extreme version of the sick role.

- He is no longer just *seeking* medical advice – he has handed himself over entirely to a medical regime.

- He is not just *excused* normal duties – he is completely removed from normal life.

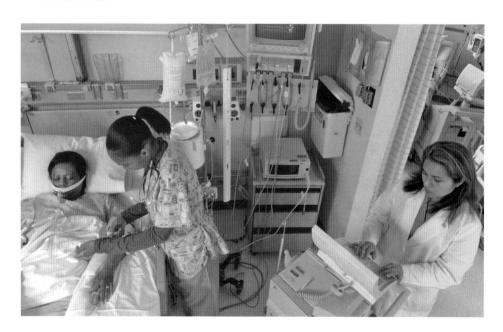

The hospital patient role

The hospital has taken over responsibility for all aspects of Anwar's health and daily living. This includes personal things such as what and when he eats and drinks, what he wears, personal cleanliness, toileting, and so on. All the daily activities which have given structure and a sense of purpose to Anwar's life are gone, leaving him with little to do but stick to hospital routines. He is 'another patient', like all the rest. (Later in K101 you will be introduced to Erving Goffman's concept of the 'total institution', which explains the effects of such all-enveloping environments on those who live and work in them.)

Anwar's transition into the hospital patient role would have started with the strangeness of riding in an ambulance. Then there was the odd experience of lying on a trolley, while other people bustled about. Instead of sitting up and looking people in the eye like an ordinary person, he would be lying like a body waiting to be treated. After that, he was wheeled to the ward, as if he were helpless. Then he was asked to take off the clothes in which he looked and felt like himself and put on a hospital robe which would make him look and feel like a patient. Then five strangers introduced themselves to him in succession. All, no doubt, seeming very much 'at home' in the hospital, which would make him all the more aware of being 'an outsider'. These are typical steps in the process of:

- shedding your identity as an active, competent member of society
- acquiring a passive identity as someone with a particular medical condition.

As a nurse in a research study observed:

> You get somebody who is an executive or up-market business person, or anybody – doesn't matter who they are – come into hospital and all of a sudden they're subservient, you know. No matter who they are. It's the way you treat them. You bring them into hospital, strip them of all their clothes, put them in pyjamas and shove them in bed and tell them to behave. And people take it!
>
> (Quoted in Lawler, 1991, p. 148)

In fact, Anwar did not realise quite how passive his patient role was meant to be, but he found out soon after the night shift came in.

Not playing the hospital patient role

Staff Nurse Jasvinder Kaur was having a frustrating shift. With several emergency admissions, handover had been difficult, the ward was short-staffed, some supplies had not been delivered and the computer system was playing up. When she came to check Anwar's blood sugar and give him his insulin, he said brusquely that he had already done this himself. She told him firmly that he should not self-medicate in hospital, and that he ought to have handed over his testing kit. She took away his kit and his insulin, and when Anwar asked why, she said it was a hospital rule.

In the controlled biomedical environment of a hospital, with its commitment to systematically recorded observations and medication, to self-medicate would mess up the system (unless it were a ward where self-medication was explicitly allowed). Also, ward staff have taken on responsibility for Anwar's condition when he arrives at the operating theatre next morning. However, Anwar has, for some months, been treated as someone who understands diabetes and is competent to carry out his own tests and injections. Now he finds himself in a much more passive role. By doing what Nurse Richards trained him to do at home, he finds himself breaking rules and being told off by Nurse Jasvinder:

> Hospitals are complex social environments that can disrupt patients' natural transition to the sick role … This is particularly true when patients and health care professionals have different expectations of patients' hospital role. The current emphasis on encouraging patients to participate in their own care is in direct conflict with one of the obligations of their sick role, which is to unquestioningly comply with the opinions of health professionals.

(Faulkner and Aveyard, 2002, p. 35)

As you can see, the hospital patient role (the extreme version of the sick role) is at odds with the expert patient role advocated within community health care. For Anwar, this peculiarly passive role and the unfamiliar hospital world, devoted to biomedical science and devoid of family and friends, provide a very difficult context in which to come to terms with the operation he is about to undergo.

4.3 Care roles in hospital

Although Anwar has been given the privilege of rapid access to the benefits of biomedical science, he is feeling distraught. As well as medical treatment he needs care and understanding.

Caring support

Ella Platt, the health care assistant on the night shift, had worked many times with patients waiting for operations and she could see how agitated Anwar was. She was careful to approach him respectfully as she went about her tasks – taking and recording his temperature, offering him a drink, tidying up his bed and showing him to the toilet. Later, he seemed to relax a bit and they struck up a conversation. Anwar started to ask her questions, but when he asked whether his operation was really necessary she said he would have to speak to the staff nurse about that. Ella went to ask Nurse Jasvinder, but she was extremely busy and said she would talk to Anwar later. Ella felt sorry for Anwar because she knew how anxious he was. She knew it might be a long time before Nurse Jasvinder had a spare moment.

Would it be better for Ella to talk with Anwar about his operation, as she is available and Jasvinder is not? What exactly can a health care assistant (HCA) do?

Reader

Activity 16   The role of the health care assistant
Allow about 30 minutes

Find Chapter 18, 'Patient safety and quality of care: the role of the health care assistant', by Hugh McKenna, Felicity Hasson and Sinead Keeney in the Reader (pages 147–154).

Read:

- the 'Introduction'
- the section headed 'HCA role evolution'
- the first eight lines of the section 'Nursing accountability for the HCA'.

Health care assistant and registered nurse working together

As you read, look for answers to these questions:

(a) How many HCAs are there estimated to be?

(b) What types of work were proposed for HCAs by the UKCC in 1988?

(c) What types of work were HCAs reported as doing in the late 1990s and early 2000s?

(d) How have the boundaries between the work of doctors, registered nurses (RNs) and HCAs shifted?

(e) When HCAs carry out care work, who is responsible?

(f) When and where was this chapter originally published?

Comment

(a) The article says that it's hard to get accurate information, but quotes an estimate of half a million HCAs in the UK. (NHS statistics for 2006 show 358,000 staff in the category 'Support to clinical staff', but this includes some clerical, administrative and maintenance staff: The Information Centre, 2007, p. 3.)

(b) The UKCC proposed that HCAs would be involved with housekeeping, clerical tasks and maintenance of the ward environment.

(c) In practice, by the early 2000s, many HCAs were routinely providing bedside nursing of a kind previously carried out by qualified nurses and student nurses.

(d) There appears to be a trend for nurses to take over some of the tasks of doctors, while HCAs take over some nurse tasks.

(e) When care work is carried out by an HCA, it is formally under the supervision of a registered nurse – although it is clear from the article that, with staffing pressures, supervision can sometimes be rather sketchy.

(f) See the learning skills box below.

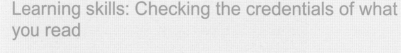

Learning skills: Checking the credentials of what you read

Reader

You should not trust everything you read. It is always important to check *when* articles or books were published and how *reliable* they are likely to be. It is called checking provenance. (There is a section on checking the provenance of websites on page 239 of *The Good Study Guide*.)

The chapter you read was originally published in 2004 as an article in the *Journal of Nursing Management* (or the JNM). The JNM is a respected academic journal and its articles are refereed – that is, they are sent to experts in the field to be approved before being published. If you had any doubts, you could look up the journal's website for information about it – for example, who is on the editorial board.

Ella was right not to talk with Anwar about medical matters because she does not have biomedical training. She carries out general caring tasks, and is supposed to leave tasks that require biomedical knowledge to a registered nurse. A research study into the views of RNs and HCAs on the difference between the two roles, found that 'certain perceived higher level tasks' were reserved for RNs:

> For instance, wound dressings were consistently reported as being the RN's job:
>
> > 'But there is much more to checking a dressing than just changing it ... there are lots of other things to think of. HCAs are just taught to do a dressing but there are so many other things involved … the environment, the patient's psychological state and such things … you get that from 3 years of training and the rest from your experience and so it's not enough to have a crash course in wound care without the underlying knowledge.' (Junior RN …)

(Spilsbury and Meyer, 2004, p. 416)

However, the study also found that:

> … interview data (verified by observation) showed the RN role to be moving away from the bedside to carry out other care-related activities, such as, technical duties, paperwork, computer care planning, liaison with other health care professionals (hospital and community) and discharge planning.

(Spilsbury and Meyer, 2004, p. 414)

Two staff nurses, Jennifer Stokes and Amy Warden, argue that:

> Health care is becoming increasingly technology-orientated, but the basic care of providing for human needs cannot be overlooked. The expansion of nurses' roles means that they are becoming more responsible for technical care traditionally undertaken by medical practitioners and have become co-ordinators of care. Essential care, for example, assisting patients to have a wash or talking through their anxieties … [is] therefore a gap for HCAs to fill …

(Stokes and Warden, 2004, p. 37)

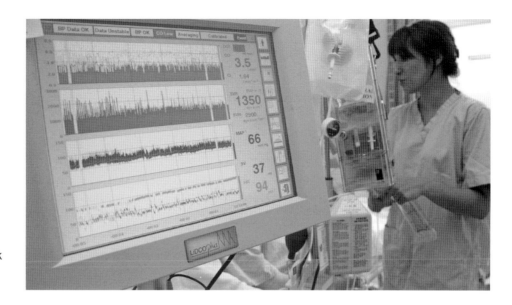

Registered nurses work increasingly with high-tech equipment

Patients' perceptions of the roles, according to a research study, are that:

> 'doctors discuss treatment and medication', 'the nurses give out tablets and work on the computer', and the 'HCAs provide assistance, make beds, take urine away and make cups of tea'. There was consensus that the HCAs were most involved in direct care.
>
> (Hancock and Campbell, 2006, p. 40)

A staff nurse like Jasvinder has such a demanding role that Ella, the HCA, may be better able to observe changes in Anwar's condition. She is certainly more likely to have the opportunity to get to know him. As one HCA in a research study said:

> Patients talk to HCAs. They might see the registered nurse but not talk to them. They want someone who is there – talking, laughing and holding their hand – not sitting behind a computer.
>
> (Quoted in Spilsbury and Meyer, 2004, p. 415)

By getting to know Anwar, Ella is more likely than Jasvinder to know how he is feeling and what his concerns are. She will be able to help him to feel less alone in an alien environment – more part of the community of the ward, more 'cared for', and not just a body waiting for biomedical attention. To thrive in hospital, Anwar needs more than a biomedical *cure*. He also needs *care*:

> The role of the HCA has progressed from being an undervalued 'dead-end job', to a skilled role that is becoming increasingly recognised in health care.
>
> (Stokes and Warden, 2004, p. 37)

Nevertheless Ella, as an HCA, is supervised by Jasvinder, a registered nurse. And Jasvinder, traditionally, would defer to doctors within a hierarchy of biomedical expertise:

> … nurses have traditionally been seen as adjuncts to the doctor rather than as practitioners in their own right.
>
> (Jones, 1994, p. 32)

The organisation of roles and responsibilities in hospitals has tended to be tightly structured and strictly observed. Given the weight of responsibility for the welfare of patients, the biomedical regime and the complexities of specialisation, this is understandable. However, new ways of working are emerging which involve less hierarchy and more team working. The following account from the *British Journal of Nursing* illustrates hierarchy first, then team working:

> As a ritual the ward round is the prime example ... of medical power in the hospital ...
>
> In my first example ... the patients on a ward were just about to start their lunches. The consultant was having difficulty getting access onto the ward as the security system at the entrance was faulty. When at last a nursing auxiliary noticed and admitted him, he stormed up to her and shouted in her face. He then commenced his ward round in a very abrupt and confrontational manner, now and again shouting instructions at the ward sister.
>
> In the second example, the medical consultant joined the rest of the care team in a quiet room to discuss the patients' cases before commencing his ward round. He encouraged all the members of the team to give him feedback and then asked permission of the ward sister to carry out his round. At the end of the round, certain patients and relatives joined him and the ward sister in the day room for a more private and intimate discussion about their treatment and prognosis.

(Castledine, 2005, p. 625)

The nurse–doctor
working relationship

The first example portrays a hierarchical way of working:

- involving instructions being given and carried out
- in which communication is from the top down
- so it relies on all-knowing doctors, obedient nurses and passive patients.

(Admittedly, it is a rather bad-tempered example. Hierarchical working can also be polite and calm.)

The second example portrays a consultative and collaborative system:

- in which knowledge is shared
- the strengths of all participants are brought into play
- and work is driven by a team ethos.

Each system has strengths and weaknesses. However, as health care becomes more complex and sophisticated, simple command hierarchies tend to lack flexibility and team working comes to the fore.

Farewell to Anwar

There is much more that could be told about Anwar's story:

- his period of recovery in hospital, during which he became friendly with several of the staff
- having an artificial limb fitted, then being trained in using it
- the courses of physiotherapy to prepare him for re-engaging with active life, and also occupational therapy to prepare him for adapting to life without his lower leg
- the complicated planning for his return home – arranging adaptations to his house, supplying him with a wheelchair, setting up support for him and Hansa as they adjusted to his new care needs
- finally, Anwar's achievement of a stable condition and a satisfying life.

But this is more than we have space for – and you will, in any case, read about these kinds of things (although not about Anwar) in the rest of the course.

Key points

- Health care has been completely transformed by biomedical science, particularly over the last century.
- For the purposes of acute care, priority is given in hospitals to the biomedical model – focusing more on treating the body than on the person and their life.
- Being a hospital patient is an extreme version of the 'sick role'.
- The traditional 'hospital patient' role is at odds with the more active 'expert patient' role.
- As acute care has changed, registered nurses tend to spend increasing amounts of time working with advanced medical equipment and computer systems, and have taken over some of the former tasks of doctors.

- Meanwhile, health care assistants have increasingly taken over bedside caring tasks from registered nurses, although continuing to work under their supervision.

- Health care roles in hospital were traditionally organised in a hierarchy of biomedical expertise, but new forms of team working have emerged in recent times.

Learning skills: Following up references

In the last few pages there have been a lot of quotations from articles and books. What if you wanted to read a bit more from one of them – say the Spilsbury and Meyer piece? How would you set about it? The first thing is to go to the list of references at the end of this unit. Look at it now and see if you can find Spilsbury and Meyer, 2004.

References follow strict formats (although the formats vary a bit from academic subject to subject). They always begin with the writer's surname and initials, then the date of publication, then the title, and so on. You'll see that the Spilsbury and Meyer article was published in 2004 in the *Journal of Nursing Management*.

Once you have the reference details, you can often find an article you are interested in by searching online. You could try logging on to OU StudentHome, then click the Library link, and click Search. Then type 'journal of nursing management' into the search box and click Search. This should bring up a listing which includes the JNM (perhaps more than once). Try clicking the links to see whether they lead you to the article on health care assistants.

Alternatively, you could use Google Scholar. Just putting Spilsbury and Meyer into the search may get you straight to the article. However, you might not be able to get free access to it without going through your university library membership. Journals vary in their accessibility policies.

5 Health care in changing times

Health care has changed dramatically over the past century. We have already noted one powerful driver of this change – the relentless advance of biomedical science, producing a continual stream of new treatments. In this final section we look at three other drivers:

- changing ideas about what health is
- changes within our society
- changes in government policy.

5.1 Changing ideas of health

Health seems a simple idea, but is surprisingly tricky to pin down. The biomedical approach tends to lead to a view of health as 'absence of disease'. But this is a negative definition – if you are not ill, then you are healthy. It provides nothing positive to aim for. Nor does it take into account the many non-medical aspects of health, such as diet, sanitation, housing, or income levels.

In 1946 the World Health Organization (WHO) agreed a much more ambitious definition of health, which it has never since amended:

> Health is a state of complete physical, mental and social well-being and not merely the absence of disease or infirmity.

(WHO, 1946)

The implication is that fighting disease and infirmity is not enough. People must also be supported to feel fully well in body and mind and capable of living well. This takes us beyond the biomedical model. According to Professor of Health Linda Jones, 'The WHO definition connects to a social model of health, which emphasises the environmental causes of health and disease' (Jones, 1994, p. 12). The social model promotes the idea that health care is not just concerned with 'curing' illness, but is also concerned with *preventing* illness and *promoting* good health. Jones notes, however, that 'The social model does not abandon the medical model but adds to it' (Jones, 1994, p. 34).

The WHO definition of health presents an admirable goal which raises sights above very basic health care provision. However, in requiring *complete* well-being and *absence* of disease or infirmity, it excludes most people from being counted as healthy. And what about Anwar Malik with his long-term condition and physical impairment? Is he to think of himself as permanently *un*healthy? David Matthews clearly expects *his* diabetes patients to be able to live fulfilling, healthy lives.

Activity 17   Can a person with diabetes be healthy?

Allow about 10 minutes

Read the story of Andie in the box below. It is taken from the Diabetes UK website. As you read, ask yourself:

Is Andie healthy or unhealthy?

Andie on holiday

I look forward to getting my 70-year medal

I have had Type 1 diabetes since I was three years old, and do not know any other way of life other than eating healthily, and respecting my medication regimen. To me, being diabetic is about living a healthy life, taking responsibility, and respecting that fact that while you can do the majority of things other people do, you always bear in mind the fact that you just have to take a little more care.

I have no complications and have been diabetic for 25 years now, and have done all the stuff my mates have done, including uni and clubbing holidays in Ibiza. Diabetes has not affected my work at all.

[...]

I am proud of being diabetic and managing it to the extent that I do, it is part of my identity. I look forward in my old age to collecting my medal for successfully managing 70 years of insulin treatment – and, as my partner has joked, will likely stubbornly refuse a cure if it becomes available, just to get my medal!

(Diabetes UK, 2007)

Write down what you think.

Comment

Andie obviously sees herself as healthy. Indeed, she suggests that *because* she has diabetes she *has* to live a healthy life.

Thinking about someone like Andie makes clear how unsatisfactory it is to equate health with absence of disease. She is proud of the state of health she achieves through controlling her diabetes. So for her, and indeed for the majority of people, health is something they hope to achieve *even though* some parts of their bodies are functioning less than perfectly. So while the WHO definition of health is helpful in shifting thinking beyond the biomedical model to include the social model, it has its problems. Indeed, the more you think about health, the harder it is to pin down exactly what it is, although instinctively you may feel you know.

We can also note in passing that the concept of the 'sick role' does not really fit long-term disease. The sick role refers to the excusals and expectations that apply during a period of stepping back from normal life. But someone with a long-term condition is not stepping back – they are living their normal life. So they are *not* claiming the sick role.

For similar reasons, we have used the term 'condition', rather than illness, to describe Anwar's diabetes (after the initial period of diagnosis and starting treatment). The important thing for Anwar is to be able to live his life well and keep his diabetes regime in the background. To be permanently ill is a contradiction. Anwar's aim is to be as well as he can while managing his long-term condition.

Neither sickness nor health is straightforward, but what is increasingly recognised is that health is a broad concept. It has to do with both minimising disease and maximising psychological and social well-being.

5.2 Changes in society

Ideas about health change, but so also does *health itself*:

> The ageing of populations, driven by falling infant and child death rates, smaller family sizes and longer average adult life expectancies, has – along with the social and economic forces associated with industrialisation, urbanisation, female emancipation and shifts from manual to 'knowledge-based' occupations – been linked with profound changes in healthcare needs ...

> (Taylor and Bury, 2007, p. 27)

Diseases of poverty, for example, have been overtaken by diseases of plenty – so that obesity has replaced malnutrition as a major concern. And instead of the physical stresses of hard labour, more people suffer from psychological stress and diseases of inactivity. However, health overall has improved significantly, certainly in terms of longer lifespans. And although biomedicine has played a part in this, other key factors have been rising income levels, better housing and improved diet.

One consequence of longer lives is steadily rising numbers of older people, and a growing need for health care for them. Also, more people are surviving with conditions which require long-term health care support – the kind of support requiring collaboration between service users and health care professionals.

Another area of change is people's attitudes to professional experts and to their own rights to health care:

> ... as average levels of income and education have risen, health professionals have had to accept significant changes in their social status relative to those for whom they care ... reforming paternalistic relationships in healthcare, and enabling service providers to work in closer partnership with health service users ...

> (Taylor and Bury, 2007, p. 41)

Living conditions in the 1930s

In other words, doctors can no longer rely on patients being overawed by their education and status. Patients increasingly feel they have a right to high quality health care and are confident about finding and understanding for themselves information about diseases and treatments. So there has been a shift of emphasis from paternalistic relationships between health care professionals and service users to partnerships in which the doctor offers advice and support, often to an expert patient. (Think back to 'compliance' versus 'concordance' in Section 3.3, p. 00.)

There has also been huge expansion of professional expertise in areas such as physiotherapy, occupational therapy, radiography, dietetics, chiropody, orthoptics, art therapy, social work and pharmacy. This has undermined the notion of a simple biomedical hierarchy of doctors, nurses and auxiliaries. Health care is increasingly delivered by teams of professionals covering a wide range of expertise (as, for example, when arrangements were made for Anwar to return from hospital back into the community). This requires collaborative, 'interprofessional' styles of working, as illustrated by the second ward round described by Castledine (see Section 4.3, p. 00).

We can pick out three trends here, each of which represents a shift away from the biomedical model of a generation ago:

- from *hierarchies* to *team working* among health care professionals
- from *paternalism* to *partnership* in doctor–patient relationships
- the rise of the *expert patient*.

DVD

Activity 18   Reconfiguring the biomedical model

Allow about 12 minutes

You can now hear David Matthews giving his views, as a leading biomedical scientist and clinician, on these three trends.

Go to the DVD and find Block 1, Unit 2, Activity 18.

Comment

According to David Matthews' account, the biomedical model has been reconfigured over the past forty years, becoming more open and inclusive of other health care professions and of patients themselves. He gives illustrations of all three of the above trends and is supportive of each.

In the final section we see how these trends are reflected in national policy on health care.

5.3 Change in the health services

The early 2000s saw significant developments in government health care policy:

- In 2003 *Partnership for Care: Scotland's Health White Paper* (Scottish Executive, 2003) was published.
- This was followed in 2006 by *Our Health, Our Care, Our Say: A New Direction for Community Services*, a White Paper for England and Wales (DH, 2006).

What are White Papers?

White papers are documents produced by the Government setting out details of future policy on a particular subject. A White Paper will often be the basis for a Bill to be put before Parliament. The White Paper allows the Government an opportunity to gather feedback before it formally presents the policies as a Bill.

(Source: United Kingdom Parliament, 2007)

Both White Papers set out a case for major changes in the way health care services are provided. And what they propose reflects exactly the changes in health care needs, attitudes and relationships that we have been discussing.

Team working

The White Paper for England and Wales notes that:

> There has been a change in emphasis in delivery of primary care, with more team-based approaches involving nurses and other professionals.

(DH, 2006, p. 65)

Paternalism to partnership

It also promotes the idea of self-care:

> People will be supported to take better control of their care and condition through a wide range of initiatives. These include a major new focus on self care and self-management.

(DH, 2006, p. 112)

Rise of the expert patient

Specifically, it advocates support for the 'expert patient':

> The Expert Patients Programme (EPP) provides training for people with a chronic condition to develop the skills they need to take effective control of their lives.

(DH, 2006, p. 112)

The service user perspective

The two White Papers also emphasise the importance of the service user perspective, which we discussed in Section 3. Scotland's White Paper says:

> Looking at services from a patient's point of view underpins everything that we are seeking to do in the health service.

(Scottish Executive, 2003, p. 7)

Bringing the hospital into the community

Particularly interesting, in the light of all that you have read in this unit, is the underlying strategy of the two White Papers: to redefine the relationship between primary care in the community and secondary care in hospitals. Scotland's White Paper argues that:

> One of the historic problems of the health service has been the split between primary care and secondary care …

(Scottish Executive, 2003, p. 5)

Meanwhile, the White Paper for England and Wales says that:

> ... [the] aim is to bring about a sustained realignment of the whole health and social care system. Far more services will be delivered – safely and effectively – in settings closer to home ...

(DH, 2006, p. 17)

As David Nicholson, Chief Executive of the NHS, explained in a letter to House of Commons MPs:

> ... more care will be conducted outside the four walls of hospitals. Primary care practices are increasingly providing a range of services such as minor surgery.
>
> [In] hospital, more and more procedures are carried out as day cases. Of those patients who do have to stay in hospital for longer than one night ... we are witnessing a long-term downward trend in the average length of stay.

(Nicholson, 2006)

In effect, the 'sick role' is being redefined. Instead of people withdrawing from everyday life to play a passive role in hospital, they will be encouraged, where possible, to remain active – retaining their normal links with the world, while being supported in taking responsibility for their own care.

National Service Frameworks

With the shifting of health care out of hospitals into the community, the White Papers recognise the need for:

> A comprehensive framework ... [for] developing local strategies to support self care for people with long-term conditions ...

(DH, 2006, p. 112)

So, for example, National Service Frameworks for Diabetes have been set up for England, Wales, Northern Ireland and Scotland.

To see how these new ideas for delivering health care are intended to work, your final activity in this unit is to read a shortened version of a report by Sue Roberts, National Director for Diabetes (England).

Resources

Activity 19   Reshaping diabetes treatment

Allow about 45 minutes

Find Resource 4, 'Working together for better diabetes care', by Sue Roberts in the Resources Book. Read it, looking for examples of the following:

- team working
- partnership with patients
- schemes to encourage 'expert patients'
- connecting hospital to community.

Highlight or underline them as you find them.

When you have finished, write a few notes in answer to these questions:

(a) In what ways did Sue Roberts' experience in the late 1970s reflect the traditional biomedical model of health care?

(b) How, according to Sue Roberts, were services reorganised to address the problems?

(c) Are Sue Roberts' case studies and proposals compatible with what you have read in this unit?

Comment

Examples of team working:

- Bolton Diabetes Centre: primary and secondary care coordinated so that most care is provided in GP surgeries, with specialists visiting regularly to deal with complex cases
- Hillingdon pharmacies
- Leamington Sikhs – 'Temple to Table'.

Partnership with patients:

- Care planning is undertaken as a partnership.

Supporting expert patients:

- DAFNE programme
- DESMOND programme.

Connecting hospital to community:

- Southport and Ormskirk
- Bolton.

(a) **The biomedical model in the late 1970s.** Sue Roberts had five minutes per patient to diagnose, prescribe and advise. Meanwhile, one patient had to take a day out of ordinary life and the consultation took place within the world of biomedicine – cut off from the everyday world in which he had to manage his illness. There was no team working with local health care professionals and no time to enter into partnership with this catastrophically ill-informed patient.

(b) **How these problems were addressed.** Diabetes clinics within GP surgeries were set up, with hospital specialists linked to primary care teams. Diabetes registers and regular check-ups were instituted.

(c) **Is Sue Roberts' account compatible with this unit?** Very much so. She recounts changes over 30 years from the traditional biomedical model to a variety of innovative schemes which break down barriers between health care professions and between professionals and patients. Patients are supported in becoming self-caring, expert patients.

With growing numbers of people needing long-term health care, a realignment is taking place to provide health care services more flexibly. Old boundaries between community-based primary care and hospital-based specialist care are being redefined to create coordinated local teams which can support patients in taking control of their own care.

Key points

- Health is not a straightforward concept. It involves minimising disease and maximising psychological and social well-being.

- Levels of health are affected by biomedical advances and also by social change, such as income levels, quality of housing, diet and patterns of exercise.

- As society changes, the paternalistic relationships of the traditional biomedical model of health care are giving way to partnership and support for patient expertise.

- Recent government policy supports these less hierarchical forms of health care relationships.

- Government policy aims to break down barriers between hospitals and community care, shifting acute care, where possible, close to the everyday world of the service user.

- Recent trends in diabetes care (as promoted by National Service Frameworks for Diabetes) provide excellent examples of these government policies in action.

Conclusion

In this unit you have seen that both illness and health are complicated ideas. Both have biological, social and psychological aspects. Consequently, health care involves more than medical 'cures' – it has to take account of people's lives and lifestyles within their particular cultural and social contexts. You saw what this means in practical terms by following the case of Anwar Malik. You saw how community health care is now delivered through multi-professional primary health care teams, with links to local networks of care and support and, increasingly, with ties to local hospitals. And you saw the growing emphasis on the service user perspective and on developing egalitarian relationships between service users and health care professionals. Finally, you saw how health care is continually changing as society changes and new needs, attitudes and expectations emerge.

Learning skills: What does it take to be a skilful learner?

You have now completed your second unit. Congratulations!

But how do you feel about it? Do you think you have learned well? Do you regard yourself as a skilful student, or do you feel you are just taking a step at a time and hoping for the best? Given that you are going to be investing a lot of time in studying over the next few months, it is important to pause and think about the effectiveness of your approach to studying. To help you do this, read Sections 1.5 to 1.7 of *The Good Study Guide* (pages 18–26).

Reader

End-of-unit checklist

Studying this unit should have helped you to:

- be aware of biological, social and psychological aspects of illness and health
- be aware that primary health care is provided through a network of services within the community
- be aware of the role of hospitals as centres of acute care for rare, complicated and serious conditions and emergency treatment for serious injuries
- understand the impact of the hospital environment on the experiences of patients and care staff
- understand the importance of the service user perspective in ensuring socially, culturally and psychologically sensitive health care services
- be aware of the central role of biomedicine in shaping modern health care, but also of recent realignments of the biomedical model to be more inclusive of other aspects of health care
- understand why health care services for long-term conditions need to be negotiated as partnerships between health care professionals and self-caring, expert patients
- be aware of the shift in emphasis away from hospital-based care towards community-based provision.

References

Bissell, P., May, C.R. and Noyce, P.R. (2004) 'From compliance to concordance: barriers to accomplishing a re-framed model of health care interactions', *Social Science and Medicine*, vol. 58, no. 4, pp. 851–62.

Castledine, G. (2005) 'The relationship between nurses and doctors', *British Journal of Nursing*, vol. 14, no. 11, p. 625.

Danescourt Surgery (2007) *Primary Health Care Team* [online], www.wales.nhs.uk/sites3/page.cfm?orgid=706&pid=21501 (Accessed 26 February 2008).

Department of Health (DH) (2006) *Our Health, Our Care, Our Say: A New Direction for Community Services*, Norwich, The Stationery Office; also available online at www.dh.gov.uk/en/Publicationsandstatistics/Publications/ PublicationsPolicyAndGuidance/DH_4127453 (Accessed 26 February 2008).

Diabetes UK (2007) *I Look Forward to Getting My 70-Year Medal – I Might Even Refuse a Cure!* [online], www.diabetes.org.uk/Guide-to-diabetes/Your-stories/Diabetes-stories/I-look-forward-to-getting-my-70-year-medal---I-might-even-refuse-a-cure- (Accessed 26 February 2008).

Faulkner, M. and Aveyard, B. (2002) 'Is the hospital sick role a barrier to patient participation?', *Nursing Times*, vol. 98, no. 24, pp. 35–6.

Glenton, C. (2003) 'Chronic back pain sufferers – striving for the sick role', *Social Science and Medicine*, vol. 57, no. 11, pp. 2243–52.

Hancock, H. and Campbell, S. (2006) 'Developing the role of the health care assistant', *Nursing Standard*, vol. 20, no. 49, pp. 35–41.

Jones, L. (1994) *The Social Control of Health and Health Work*, Basingstoke, Macmillan.

Lawler, J. (1991) *Behind the Screens: Nursing Somology, and the Problem of Body*, Edinburgh, Churchill Livingstone.

Lawton, J., Ahmad, N., Hallowell, N., Hanna, L. and Douglas, M. (2005) 'Perceptions and experiences of taking oral hypoglycaemic agents among people of Pakistani and Indian origin: qualitative study', *British Medical Journal*, 330, pp. 1247–50.

Medical Schools & Nursing Colleges Worldwide (2007) *Becoming a General Practitioner: General Practice in the UK* [online], www.medical-colleges.net/gp.htm (Accessed 28 February 2008).

NHS Choices (2007) *About NHS Services: NHS GPs/Doctors* [online], www.nhs.uk/AboutNHSservices/doctors/Pages/DoctorsSummary.aspx (Accessed 17 December 2007).

NHS Direct (2007a) *Health and Medical Glossary* [online], www.nhsdirect.nhs.uk/glossary (Accessed 26 February 2008).

NHS Direct (2007b) *Health Encyclopaedia. Diabetes: Introduction* [online], www.nhsdirect.nhs.uk/articles/article.aspx?articleId=128 (Accessed 26 February 2008).

NHS Direct (2007c) *What Are Primary Care Trusts (PCTs)?* [online], www.nhsdirect.nhs.uk/articles/article.aspx?articleId=1078 (Accessed 26 February 2008).

NHS Direct (2007d) *What Services Do Hospitals Provide?* [online], www.nhsdirect.nhs.uk/articles/article.aspx?articleId=1089 (Accessed 26 February 2008).

NHS National Diabetes Support Team (2006) *Diabetic Foot Guide* [online], www.diabetes.nhs.uk/downloads/NDST_Diabetic_Foot_Guide.pdf (Accessed 26 February 2008).

Nicholson, D. (2006) *Letter to MPs*, November 2006 [online], www.dh.gov.uk/ prod_consum_dh/idcplg?IdcService=GET_FILE&dID=122724&Rendition=Web (Accessed 26 February 2008).

Parsons, T. (1951) *The Social System*, Glencoe, IL, The Free Press.

Royal College of General Practitioners (2003) *The Primary Health Care Team*, Information Sheet No. 21 [online], www.rcgp.org.uk/pdf/ISS_INFO_21_OCT03.pdf (Accessed 26 February 2008).

Royal Pharmaceutical Society Working Party (1997) *From Compliance to Concordance: Achieving Shared Goals in Medicine Taking. Report of the Working Party*, London, Royal Pharmaceutical Society of Great Britain/Merck, Sharp and Dohme.

Scottish Executive (2003) *Partnership for Care: Scotland's Health White Paper* [online], www.scotland.gov.uk (Accessed 26 February 2008).

Shilling, C. (2002) 'Culture, the "sick role" and the consumption of health', *British Journal of Sociology*, vol. 53, no. 4, pp. 621–38

Spilsbury, K. and Meyer, J. (2004) 'Use, misuse and non-use of health care assistants: understanding the work of health care assistants in a hospital setting', *Journal of Nursing Management*, vol. 12, no. 6, pp. 411–18.

Stokes, J. and Warden, A. (2004) 'The changing role of the health care assistant', *Nursing Standard*, vol. 18, no. 51, pp. 33–7.

Taylor, D. and Bury, M. (2007) 'Chronic illness, expert patients and care transition', *Sociology of Health and Illness*, vol. 29, no. 1, pp. 27–45.

The Information Centre (2007) *Staff in the NHS 2006: An Overview* [online], www.ic.nhs.uk/webfiles/publications/nhsstaff2006/NHS%20Staff%20leaflet.pdf (Accessed 26 February 2008).

United Kingdom Parliament (2007) *Glossary – Parliamentary Jargon Explained* [online], www.parliament.uk/about/glossary.cfm?ref=whitepa_9927 (Accessed 17 December 2007).

World Health Organization (WHO) (1946) *Preamble to the Constitution of the World Health Organization as Adopted by the International Health Conference, New York, 19 June – 22 July 1946* [online], www.who.int/suggestions/faq/en (Accessed 26 February 2008).

Websites

www.diabetes.org.uk (Accessed 26 February 2008).

www.diabetes-healthnet.ac.uk (Accessed 26 February 2008).

www.nhsdirect.nhs.uk (Accessed 26 February 2008).

www.nhs24.com (Accessed 26 February 2008).

Unit 3

Social care in the community

Prepared for the course team by Jan Walmsley

Contents

Introduction

In this third unit of Block 1, you will explore social care, a third major area of provision in health and social care. You left Anwar Malik at the end of Unit 2 facing life back in the community after his spell in hospital. He is going to need quite a lot of support beyond that which can be supplied by his wife, but he is well enough to leave hospital, so he will fall into the remit of community-based services.

All societies face the challenge of supporting people who, for a variety of reasons, are unable to function without support or supervision. This is broadly the role of social care, although, as you will see as the unit unfolds, there is a lively debate about who needs and deserves state-supported social care. As discussed in Unit 1, much work that would otherwise need to be supplied by paid carers goes on in families, and there is a lot of interest in how families can continue to perform this vital service. But some families struggle to provide adequate support, some people prefer not to rely on families, there are crises, and there are always people who fall outside the care of families for a whole raft of reasons. This is where social care comes in.

Unlike health care, however, which is largely free at the point of delivery in the UK, social care is far from a universal service, and it is rarely free. The way in which it is funded and provided is complex and varies according to where you live.

This unit will not cover the whole of social care. It is a huge area. It will instead focus on one important area of social care – home care for older people – and will follow the story of the family whom you encountered in the Unit 1 case study, as they enter the world of social care. The unit will then go behind the scenes to find out what underpins their experience.

Core questions

- How do people access social care services?
- Who decides who gets social care and who pays for it?
- What do home carers do?
- How is home care managed?
- What are Direct Payments and how do they compare with more traditional home care services?

Are you taking the IVR?

If you are studying K101 as part of the Integrated Vocational Route (IVR), don't forget to check your VQ Candidate Handbook to see which Unit 3 activities contribute to your electronic portfolio.

1 Entering the world of social care

In this unit we continue the story of the Unit 1 case study to explore what social care is and how it works. When we last encountered Ann, she had just decided, very tentatively, to ask the Social Work Department for help in caring for Angus, and had made a phone call. (Ann lives in Scotland – in England or Wales, she would have asked Adult Social Care, or something similar.) What Ann had not been expecting was a visit from a social worker asking questions about Zoe, because the school was concerned about her behaviour.

DVD

Activity 1   Journey into social care

Allow about 25 minutes

It's time to pick up Ann and Angus' story again.

Go to the DVD and find Block 1, Unit 3, Activity 1.

Comment

You now have some insight into the complexities of the journey that Ann and her family travelled in getting access to social care services, and the emotional ups and downs they experienced on the way. You have also met Yetunde, the home carer who enters their lives.

For a fuller picture of the challenges of accessing support, we return now to the article by Joyce Cavaye, who carried out the research on which the case study of Ann and Angus is based.

Resources

Activity 2   Reflecting on the journey

Allow about 15 minutes

Find Resource 1, 'Becoming and being a carer', by Joyce Cavaye in the Resources Book. You read as far as the heading 'Accessing services' for Activity 2 in Unit 1. Now read from there to the heading 'Continuation of caring: experience of services'.

Highlight key words as you read, but also keep beside you the notes you have just made for Activity 1. When new thoughts come to you, write them in the margins of your Activity 1 notes. Don't worry about making the notes messy. This is a working document. You are using it to make links between your own reactions to the audio drama and Cavaye's ideas. It is an aid to help you think.

Comment

Keep the notes you have just been working on alongside you as you read the rest of this section, which expands on the issues raised in Cavaye's article.

Ann and her family go through several stages in adjusting to being recipients of home care. Of course, every family is unique, but there are also important common themes, which we will now explore.

1.1 Accessing services

Journey into social care

As you will recall, it took a lot for Ann to pick up the phone to ask for help with Angus. She really was at the end of her tether by the time she did so. As Cavaye makes clear, it can take family carers many months, or even years, to get to this point. The barriers to asking for help are considerable. In Ann and Angus' case, the barriers were:

- lack of knowledge: not knowing where to look, or what they were entitled to expect – whereas most people know they are entitled to ask for a GP appointment or to go to Accident and Emergency, the sorts of help available in social care are less well known

- pride in being able to manage: as Ann's mother had done – and fear of being labelled as failing in some way by asking for help

- resistance to recognising the severity of the situation

- resistance on Angus' part as the person being cared for: as he said, 'I don't want some stranger messing me about'

- reluctance on Ann's part, as the carer, and on the part of other family members, to opening their home to someone they didn't know

- pessimism over the type of help available: fear that the only option offered would be 'going into a home'

- uncertainty over costs.

It was a combination of factors which prompted Ann to take what seemed to her a huge step – concern over Zoe, a feeling that she simply was not going to be able to manage, worry about her relationship with Bob, and encouragement from Cheryl who had been there before.

As the conversation between Ann and Cheryl in the pub highlights, if the welfare of a child is an issue, there is likely to be more prompt attention from the authorities, whether or not it is welcome. But when a carer appears to be managing without undue risk of anyone getting badly hurt, there can be considerable delay. In 2007, a report published by the Scottish Executive found that 'Around half of Scotland's local authorities reported operating waiting lists for assessments to be completed' (Scottish Executive, 2007, p. 30). So even after summoning the courage to enquire about support, it may take a while to get a response. And having to manage her own anxiety, as well as Angus', was quite wearing for Ann.

Learning skills: Linking K101 to your own experiences and insights

Listening to the story of Ann, Angus and her family might not seem much like 'learning'. However, it allows you to use your imagination. You can enter into their experiences and think about what it is like to be involved in their situation of caring and being cared for. The reason you are able to do this is because you can make connections with your own life and draw on aspects of your own experience – even if it is different in many ways. If K101 was written just as a sequence of arguments and information, it would be a long struggle to make sense of it all and to make it stick in your memory. However, the case studies make learning easier and deeper, by drawing on what you already know and using that as a foundation to build on. The more you are able to make your own connections with the case studies in the course, the more you will bring your own imagination and insights to bear and the better you will learn. Later, when you come to writing an essay, or revising for the exam, you will find that these 'stories' of people caring and being cared for are the parts of the course that have 'stuck in your mind', because you brought them to life within your own thoughts. You will also be able to write your answers around the case studies, which makes it much easier to explain what you know and understand.

The time you spend working with case material, and thinking about it, makes a key contribution to your learning, even if it just seems like 'going along with the story'. And if you can get into the habit of quickly writing down any thoughts about the cases as they come to you, this will increase your learning. It will make it much easier to find your way back to these thoughts when you want to use them again later. Thoughts which seem very ordinary at the time can turn out to be really useful when you revisit them. Learning at degree level has a lot to do with developing a written conversation with yourself in the form of thoughts jotted in margins and on note pads. It all helps your mind to make connections between the course and your own experiences and insights.

1.2 Carers as clients

Finally, Ann and Angus got an assessment. Although it is not given detailed attention in our audio drama, the assessment is a key part of the journey into social care. It is an individual process – everyone has different needs, so each person has to be individually assessed. Not only that, both the carer and the person they care for should be assessed, as each will have different needs. The assessment will be carried out by a qualified professional called a care manager, usually a social worker or nurse. It will normally involve gathering together information and opinions, and conducting one or more interviews with the clients – both carer and the person cared for (Foster et al., 2007).

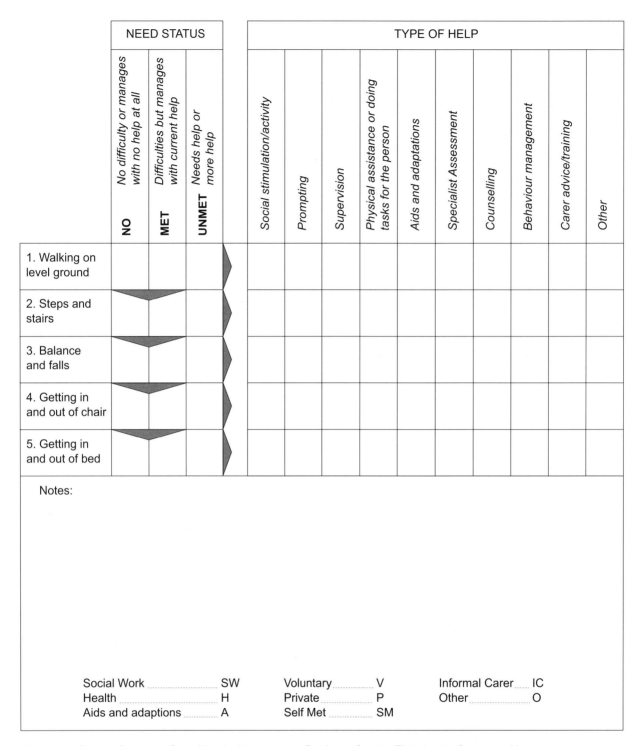

Figure 1   Extract from the *Care Needs Assessment Package for the Elderly*: the form used by care managers to assess the needs of older people (Source: CarenapE, 1999, p. 3)(Crown Copyright 1999)

Once this assessment is complete (Figure 1), and it is agreed that support is required, a care package is put together by the care manager, and it is all recorded in a care plan which states exactly what someone can expect. A copy of the care plan is left with the person whose needs have been recorded.

Social care: some technical terms

- **Assessment**: the process of determining care needs.
- **Care package**: a set of services that will meet those needs, as decided at the assessment.
- **Care manager**: the person, often a social worker or a community nurse, who manages the care package, decides the budget, finds the people and organisations to provide the services, and reviews how well it's all working.
- **Care plan**: a written record of the care that someone can expect. The recipient will sign the care plan to confirm that they have agreed to it.

The needs and wishes of the person who requires care not only should be taken into account, but should drive the assessment. There should also be a choice of services and, as just mentioned, the needs of the carer should be assessed too. However, in practice what is provided is often constrained by what is available and affordable. Leading disabled researcher Jenny Morris argues that although providing choice is the intention:

> … in practice there is no guarantee that all needs will be met. Except when they are legally obliged to act – and this is rare – a local authority can refuse to meet needs if it cannot afford to do so.

(Morris, 2004, p. 432)

A research project carried out by the Social Policy Research Unit at York examined how care managers carry out assessments. The researchers found that care managers were very aware of what was available, and the limited resources at their disposal, and therefore tried to match their assessments to what they knew

Assessment should be driven by people's needs

could be provided, rather than being led by the expressed wishes of the people they were assessing (Foster et al., 2007).

To bring this discussion down to earth, let's apply it to the case study.

You know from the drama that Angus was assessed as needing support from home carers for one hour each morning and evening, to relieve Ann. Ann was assessed as needing one week a year of respite care, to enable her to take a holiday with her family, while Angus went into a care home.

The assessment was designed to ensure that Angus' care needs were met and that Ann's needs as his carer were also addressed – but is this what they would have wanted if they really had a choice?

One way of considering this is to use a model of human needs, developed by a psychologist, Abraham Maslow.

Maslow's model of human needs

Maslow (1970) saw human needs as a hierarchy. In other words, human beings have many different needs, but until basic needs for food, drink, sleep and security are met, people are less likely to be concerned about 'higher-order' needs, such as: the need for social activities, love and friendship; the need for self-respect and recognition by others; and the need to develop and grow – what Maslow called 'self-actualisation'. Maslow was not thinking of social care assessments when he drew up this model, but it can be a useful way to consider 'care needs'.

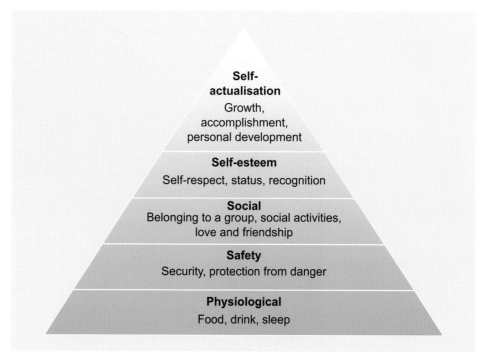

Figure 2   Maslow's hierarchy of needs (Source: adapted from Maslow, 1970)

Activity 3   Meeting needs

Allow about 10 minutes

Consider Angus' situation. Which of the needs in Maslow's hierarchy is the care package of two hours of care a day designed to meet?

Do the same for Ann.

Comment

The care package seems to address Angus' basic needs, to ensure that he will be helped in and out of bed and be washed, that his medication will be administered, and that he will be nourished. He will probably be relatively safe from harm, if he does not fall. All these are very important, but the package does not meet any of the higher-order needs shown in Maslow's hierarchy – for social activity, status and personal development.

Things may be a little better for Ann. The provision of home care should allow her to better fulfil her role as a mother, and perhaps even see some friends, while respite care may allow her a holiday; in Maslow's terms, it would meet some of her higher-order needs. More importantly from the point of view of the Social Work Department, it should enable her to continue in her caring role.

If the care package really had been driven by Angus' or Ann's wishes, it might have looked rather different. Ann might have chosen a day centre place for Angus, to free her to resume part-time work. Angus might have liked the chance to get out occasionally, meet some old friends or go on holiday.

1.3 Continuation of caring

The family had great hopes of the difference home care would make. Zoe looked forward to going shopping with her mum. It is not surprising, then, that Ann was initially disappointed. She had expected that Yetunde, the home carer, would help to lift Angus out of bed, but Yetunde refused as this was not something she was allowed to do, because it would put her health and safety at risk. Ann asked Yetunde to pick up a bit of shopping for her – but Yetunde did not have time to do this, and it wasn't in the care plan. And one hour at a time really is not long enough for a mother and daughter to go shopping together.

According to a report from the Commission for Social Care Inspection (CSCI) (2006), social care users are often frustrated by inflexibility and unreliability of services, frequent changes of staff and poorly trained staff. These are issues you will consider in more depth in Sections 3 and 4 of this unit.

DVD

Activity 4   Learning how to take advantage of support
Allow about 35 minutes

You have heard about the initial frustrations Ann and her family experienced when Yetunde started visiting them. But did things stay that way? Return now to the DVD to find out.

Find Block 1, Unit 3, Activity 4 on the DVD.

Resources

When you have completed the DVD activity, go back to Joyce Cavaye's article (Resource 1) in the Resources Book, and read from 'Continuation of caring: experience of services' to the end.

As you read, think about whether you want to add any extra points to your notes from the DVD part of this activity.

Comment

Once the family got used to her, Yetunde did make a difference. She stuck to the basic tasks in the care plan, but in little things she helped family relationships improve. She persuaded Angus to look at Zoe's cartoons – encouraging him to take more pleasure in his role as grandfather. And she accepted with good grace his request to call her 'Betty'. She also accommodated his preferences, such as liking his tea out of the blue mug! Her approach and attitude, as much as what the care plan dictated, seems to have changed things for the better.

It was not home care alone, however, that turned things around for Ann and her family.

Mutual support and specialist services

Ann and Angus got home care and, because of Angus' low income, they were not required to pay (see the article by Joyce Cavaye). It may not have been as much help as they were hoping for, but it was reliable and it did make a significant impact. However, it wasn't enough to make Ann feel better straight away. Initially, she felt worse, and was diagnosed by her doctor as needing antidepressants, as she told Cheryl in the pub. Cheryl's response was to suggest that Ann needed help for herself from a carers' group. As before, Ann resisted, but Cheryl took the initiative and made the contact for her.

The support group gave Ann general back-up and helped to make her feel less isolated with her problems. But it was also important in that it was able to offer specialist services for people who have Parkinson's disease, and for their relatives. Together with the more general home care service, then, the specialist support group seems to have made a big difference both to Ann and to Angus.

Aids and adaptations

The last element of the support the family received was aids and adaptations, such as rails in the bathroom, a Zimmer frame and the promised stairlift. Small improvements to the home can make a huge difference to people with long-term health conditions, and to their carers – if Ann does not need to lift Angus off the toilet because there is a grab rail, it could save her back as well as his dignity.

Getting aids and adaptations

We do not hear exactly how Ann managed to get their aids and appliances, but it can be difficult to get even the simplest improvement, such as grab rails. As in much of the social care system, users can face long waiting lists. In some areas, pioneering schemes have cut through the bureaucracy. In Gloucestershire, for instance, a cooperative scheme between county and district councils and housing providers enabled the employment of a team of tradesmen to make minor adaptations. In seven months the team made 777 minor adaptations, at an average fitting cost of £63. The costs compare favourably with the costs of medical treatment resulting from falls in the home.

(Source: adapted from College of Occupational Therapists, 2006)

Did you also notice how Zoe was benefiting from aids and adaptations to cope with dyslexia – pink paper and the promise of a computer?

Aids and adaptations can make a difference to people being cared for at home

1.4 A normal life?

The last we hear of Ann and her family is saying goodbye to Angus in his care home and heading off for their well-deserved holiday in Spain; a happy ending for them for the time being. It sounds as though the family is coping much better with life in respect of both Angus' needs and the needs of other family members. This is confirmed in Cavaye's article, in which she reports that Ann seemed much happier and more on top of her caring responsibilities.

Activity 5   Learning from Ann and Angus' experiences

Allow about 20 minutes

Considering what you have learned about Ann and Angus' journey into social care, think about the advice you would give Anwar and Hansa Malik as they set about rebuilding their lives following Anwar Malik's amputation. In doing this, imagine you are a well-informed friend. Use the following questions:

(a) How do people access social care services?

(b) What is it like to get home care?

(c) Are there other things people might ask for, such as support groups and specialist services?

(d) Are there aids and adaptations they could be entitled to?

(e) Is there anything else they should be thinking about?

Comment

(a) **Accessing services.** You would probably want to explain to Anwar and Hansa what social care involves. You would tell them about what they are entitled to expect: the various possible services; an assessment for Hansa as the carer, as well as for Anwar. Perhaps you would warn them that they may not get everything they would like, but that even small amounts of support can make a difference. You might point out that they will probably have to pay towards the costs. You could explain about the care plan which will define the services they will receive, and alert them to the possibility of respite care.

(b) **Home care.** Again, you might explain what this is, and how it is likely to work: that the home carer will help out and make life easier. She or he will work to a care plan, so they will know exactly what they can expect her or him to do. You might be able to head off some of the disappointment Ann felt by explaining to them that it's likely to get better as they become used to the carer, and as she or he gets to know their ways.

(c) **Support groups and specialist services.** The diabetes clinic that Anwar has been attending at Hilltop Surgery has already put him in touch with local groups for people with diabetes, and with Diabetes UK. But you might encourage Anwar to make sure that his social worker is in touch with Diabetes Nurse Richards at the clinic, to ensure that he is linked up to all appropriate support services for his new needs, following his amputation. You could also point out that prior to going into hospital, all the services and support provided were for Anwar, but now Hansa may, like Ann, find it useful to join a group.

(d) **Aids and adaptations.** This is likely to be very important as Anwar has to adjust to life with a prosthetic leg. He will probably need adaptations to help him get around: perhaps grab rails, or a ramp up to the front door. They will need to know that these are available, and how to access them.

(e) **Anything else?** The person who enabled Ann to access services was Cheryl. Could you encourage Hansa to make use of you, as someone she already knows who can steer her in the right direction as she meets the confusing maze of services in the community, and encourage her to make contact with you, whenever she needs to?

Finally, Anwar and Hansa could look for advice on the benefits they may be entitled to, such as Attendance Allowance, Disability Living Allowance, Mobility Allowance and Carer's Allowance. They could try the Department for Work and Pensions website (www.dwp.gov.uk/), or a website such as www.welfarerights.net, or a local Welfare Rights Agency.

In this section you have followed Ann and Angus as they become accustomed to being users of home care services. For them, it was not an easy journey – there were setbacks and disappointments on the way; but the story is in many ways a positive one. Between them, Yetunde the home carer, Margo who runs the Parkinson's Disease Support Group, the Parkinson's Disease Nurse Mary, and the provision of aids for Angus have made a difference to Ann and her family. The recognition that Zoe needed support to manage her dyslexia helped too. Relationships between family members have improved, and it seems that everyone played their part in making this happen. It was crucial to take the pressure off Ann, and to help enable her to realise that support was available. Once that happened, it seems that everyone else was able to rise to the occasion.

In some respects, this case study presents a rather optimistic picture of the success of home care in relieving pressure on family carers. As you will discover as you work through the unit, the consistency offered by Yetunde is not the norm.

However, we chose to feature a story in which the benefits of home care are highlighted. You will get a fuller picture as you complete your study of Unit 3, and the course overall.

Key points

- It is important to understand why carers may take a long time to recognise their own needs and ask for help.

- Before accessing home care services, users and carers need to undergo an assessment of needs. This will set out what they are entitled to expect in a care plan.

- Home carers work to the care plan. Users are not able to direct their work beyond that.

- Support from others in a similar situation is often critical to carers' well-being.

- Specialist services are often available, but not necessarily widely known about.

- Aids and adaptations to the home can be of incalculable assistance to people with disabilities or long-term health conditions.

- In reality, care services are unlikely to be able to provide for all the needs of people and their carers.

2 Social care: who decides, who pays?

In Section 1, you followed Ann and her family as they got to grips with getting help from social care services. In this section the focus will be on the bigger picture: the context in which their story is set.

The aspirations for social care in the UK are high. Here is what the English Government says in *Our Health, Our Care, Our Say: A New Direction for Community Services* (the White Paper referred to in the final section of Unit 2):

> Our central question: how do we help every individual and every community get the most out of life in a country that has never been richer in opportunity than today?
>
> […]
>
> [The White Paper] lays out a lasting and ambitious vision: by reforming and improving our community services, to create health and social care services that genuinely focus on prevention and promoting health and well-being; that deliver care in more local settings; that promote the health of all, not just a privileged few; and that deliver services that are flexible, integrated and responsive to people's needs and wishes.
>
> […]
>
> The care and support that we provide for people should enable them to make the most of their lives.
>
> (DH, 2006, pp. 3, 13)

This is a great vision, and is shared by other policy documents from Wales, Scotland and Northern Ireland. However, the resources to achieve this for everyone are often limited. The reality therefore often differs quite considerably from the intentions expressed here: that people should have choice and control; that there should be a focus on prevention as well as crisis support; and that everyone should be able to make the most of their lives, regardless of wealth, age or health status.

This discussion of social care policy will revolve around two very basic questions:

- Who decides who is eligible for social care?
- Who pays? Is social care a public responsibility to be paid for out of taxation, or is it essentially a private responsibility, to be met by the individual who needs care, or by their family?

2.1 Who decides?

Unlike health care, which, as you saw in Unit 2, is largely free at the point of use to UK residents, access to social care is restricted. Not everyone is eligible for state-provided social care – and even if they are eligible, they may well have to pay some of the costs. In this sense, social care as a public service is far more restricted than health care. Every UK citizen is potentially a user of health services. But to be a user of social care services you have to fall into some very carefully defined categories.

If social care is not available to everyone, how was it decided that Angus needed it? Before even getting as far as having a full assessment of his needs, as described in Section 1, he would need to be recognised as eligible for local authority-managed social care services. How he got to this point is what we explore next, through examination of a leaflet produced by one local authority, Manchester, setting out the rules for fair access to social care.

Resources

Activity 6 Eligibility for social care

Allow about 20 minutes

Turn now to Resource 5 in the Resources Book, where you will find Manchester City Council's *Fair Access to Care Services* leaflet. This explains who is 'eligible' for social care services in Manchester.

Read the document, and then make notes answering the following questions:

(a) Would Angus qualify for support if he lived in Manchester? What was his level of risk at the time Ann began to seek help?

(b) In Manchester, who decides what services will be provided?

(c) Would Ann qualify for support?

Comment

(a) The document makes it clear that only if risks to safety and independence are 'critical' or 'substantial' will someone be eligible for care services. If the risk is regarded as 'moderate' or 'low' then people will be helped to find their own sources of assistance. I would assess Angus as being at substantial risk for three major reasons: he cannot undertake many aspects of personal care; he cannot manage many aspects of domestic routines; and there is a significant risk of breakdown in his relationship with Ann, his carer.

(b) The services people receive are determined by the local authority once it has been decided that they fall into the 'critical or 'substantial' risk category – the leaflet states: 'If your needs are substantial or critical, we will then work with you to agree what support will be best for you ... and how to arrange the support package.'

(c) Nothing is said about support specifically for carers, but carers clearly play a highly significant role. If carers are struggling, this is likely to push people into the 'substantial' or 'critical' risk categories. Angus probably falls into the category of 'substantial' risk only because Ann is feeling unable to carry on. After all, for as long as Ann could manage his care, he was not at substantial risk.

The *Fair Access to Care Services* leaflet illustrates that social care resources provided through local authorities are targeted at those who most need help, and that the criteria for receiving that help are based on an assessment of risk. As in the case study, carers' inability to carry on is likely to be the trigger for the local authority to step in to make sure that services that will reduce the risk to people's safety and independence are provided. No wonder there is such an interest in family carers.

In Manchester, only people at substantial and critical risk are eligible to receive local authority-arranged social care. This is not the case everywhere. Who is eligible to receive social care services fluctuates over time, and indeed from place to place. Although the categories 'severe', critical', 'moderate' and 'low' are defined by the English Government, each local authority decides which categories to include – and as budgets get tighter, so do the criteria. Did you notice that the Manchester leaflet said the following?

> The range of services and the number of people we can help depends to a great degree on resources. Every year, the guidelines can be reviewed in the light of the resources available.

This means that there is no guarantee that people who are eligible now will be eligible next year. Local authorities vary as to which categories they will provide for. Manchester is fairly typical.

According to the Commission for Social Care Inspection (CSCI), in 2005:

- 6% of English councils offered an assessment to people with 'low' levels of need: that is, those who need assistance for an hour or two once or twice a week.

- 36% offered an assessment to people with 'moderate' levels of need.

- 53% offered an assessment to those with 'substantial' levels of need (Manchester was one of these).

- And 5% offered an assessment only to people with 'critical' needs – if Ann and Angus lived in one of these areas, which in 2005 were North Yorkshire, Northumberland and West Berkshire, even they might not qualify for help (CSCI, 2006).

These figures are represented in the pie chart given in Figure 3.

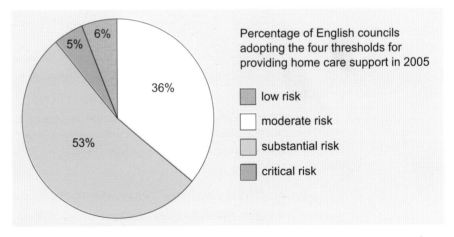

Figure 3   Percentage of English councils adopting the four thresholds for providing home care support, 2005 (Source: based on CSCI, 2006)

Learning skills: Reading pie charts

Are you tempted to skip past charts when you come to them? It would be a shame if you did skip them, because they contain important information and they show it in a way that is easier to understand than plain numbers, and also easier to remember. Pie charts help you to get things in proportion. In Figure 3 you can see straight away that in 2005 the majority of English councils set the threshold for providing an assessment at the level of 'substantial risk'. You can also see that a small proportion even provided an assessment to cases categorised as 'low risk'.

The pie chart helps you to 'take in' the figures. It helps you to see what they mean, instead of just sitting there as numbers on the page. When you come to a chart you need to take a few minutes to 'make sense' of it. You need to check that you understand what it is telling you. Here are some questions to help you check that you understand this chart.

1   Is it true that in 2005, over half of English councils offered assessments only to cases of 'substantial risk' or higher?

2   Is it true that just over a third of English councils set the threshold at 'moderate risk'?

3   Is it true that assessments had previously been more available in cases of 'low risk'?

Answers:

1   Yes – if you check with the key to the right of the chart, you can see that the huge slice that makes up a large part of the pie is the one representing 'substantial risk'.

2   Yes – the slice of pie for 'moderate risk' is 36%. One-third is about 33%, so 36% is just over a third. (Three x 33 makes 99, so three x 33% makes just about 100%.)

3   Trick question! The statement may well be true, but the pie chart does not tell you anything about this. It only gives information for 2005. To read a chart properly you have to take notice of what the chart title tells you, as well as any other information written on the chart.

Don't worry if numbers and charts aren't 'your thing'. K101 introduces them in easy stages and with plenty of explanation to help you get used to reading them.

Since the 1990s, targeting of local authority resources at people assessed to be at substantial or critical risk has intensified. The *amount* of home care people receive through local authorities has increased – but the *numbers* of people who receive services have declined:

•   In 1993, about 500,000 people received home care through local authorities.

•   In 2005, only 354,600 people received home care, but on average they got more than ten hours each (Wanless, 2006).

Increasingly, resources are targeted at the people with the highest levels of risk. It was estimated that if trends to restrict care continue, 370,000 more people would be excluded by 2009 (Wanless, 2006). They will have to find their own solutions.

Thus the answer to who decides who gets access to social care services is the local authority. They have to follow government guidelines, and they have to make difficult decisions about how to spend limited budgets – as the Manchester example shows. In effect, local authority-provided social care services are increasingly restricted to those people who are at substantial or critical risk – people like Angus.

2.2 Who pays?

How social care should be paid for is the subject of major debate (Wanless, 2006). Should it be, like health care, something everyone can expect when they need it, free of charge? Or should it be the responsibility of the individual and his or her family to pay for care? Currently, although the need for care is increasing as people live longer, public resources are targeted at people who are at substantial or critical risk. Except in a very few places, people who have low or moderate needs do not qualify for social care provided through social services. Even if they do qualify, they are 'means tested': their income is assessed to determine how much they have to pay, and how much can be funded out of local authority budgets. Depending on their income and their assets – how much they own, especially their homes – they will have to pay some or all of the costs associated with care.

Sir Derek Wanless' review *Securing Good Care for Older People: Taking a Long-term View* (2006), carried out in 2005–06 for the King's Fund, an independent charitable foundation, summarises the situation thus:

- Annually, more than one million people over the age of sixty-five, like Angus, receive publicly funded social care.

- This costs local authorities around £8 billion. Almost three-quarters of this sum is raised from national and local taxation; about one-quarter (£1.6 billion) is paid for by users.

- The National Health Service provides some care for older people (known as 'continuing care'). This costs around £3 billion per year, less than half the money spent by local authorities. NHS care is not charged for.

- A lot of people arrange and pay for their own care needs. It is hard to know how many, as there is no system for collecting this information. Sir Derek Wanless' report estimated that this private spending on social care for those aged over sixty-five was around £3.5 billion a year.

- The contribution of family carers is by far the largest. Again, this is hard to cost, but the Wanless Report estimated it to be of the value of £60 billion a year.

It is a complicated picture, but what it indicates is that, although our attention in this unit so far has been on publicly funded social care, there is a great deal of social care funded and provided by individuals and their families, a return to the theme of Unit 1.

Learning skills: Should you memorise the numbers?

You have just encountered quite a few numbers. Are you expected to try to memorise them? Basically, the answer is 'No'. That is not to say you should just skim straight over them.

- You should take a little time to think about what they mean. For instance, the first bullet point talks about one million people. How big is that figure compared with the whole population? If you have an idea that the UK population is around 62 million, then you can see that one million is somewhere between 1% and 2% of the population.

- You might also highlight some of the figures above that strike you as particularly important. Then you can find them easily if you want to come back to them.

Most people don't carry around lots of numbers in their heads. The important thing is to take in the 'general gist' of the scale of the numbers you read about, and to be able to find them if you need them again (say, to quote in an essay). As far as the end-of-course exam is concerned, you might find it useful to be able to include a number or two in your answers. But equally, you will be able get a good result without including much at all in the way of numbers. K101 is essentially about ideas rather than facts and figures.

There are three major factors which determine whether provision of social care is a public or a private responsibility:

- the person's income and overall wealth
- whether they are assessed as needing 'health' or 'social' care
- where they live – the 'postcode lottery'.

I will discuss these in turn.

Income and wealth

A person's income is taken into account when they are assessed as needing social care. If they have savings above a relatively low level (£21,000 in 2006), and need home care, they will be asked to pay towards the costs. This was not, at the time of writing, the case in Scotland, where personal care was provided free of charge, which is why Ann does not have to pay towards the costs of Yetunde's services. If they were in England or Wales they would probably have to make a contribution.

> Patricia Reynolds, aged 71, who is disabled, described the cost of being a privately funded user of care services:
>
> > It costs me £850 a month. I was paying £550 a month until last year, when the rate went up ... That pays for one hour every morning with Care Connect [a not-for-profit provider] and a further hour of care every day split between lunch, tea and bedtime, provided by the council. I'm spending my savings on this; I draw down more than £7,000 a year ... There's a lot of people in a worse situation: if they self-fund, they are paying over £1,000 a month; if they are funded by the council, their care is being cut.
>
> (Source: quoted in Butler, 2007, p. 3)

If the person is admitted to a care home, the value of their house will be taken into account also, and until the total value of their assets reduces to £21,000, they will be entirely self-funding. This usually means selling the house to pay for care.

Health care or social care

As you saw in the bullet points summary from the Wanless Report, some people get NHS 'continuing care'. There is a fierce debate over who is entitled to have long-term care paid for by the NHS. Remember that this division is crucial because health care is free, while social care is not, except for people with very few savings and assets. As anxiety grows about more older and dependent people needing care, so governments have increasingly defined long-term care as 'social care' rather than 'health care'. Sociologist Julia Twigg puts it like this:

> The division between health and social care is increasingly a division between care that is free to the individual, and that which has to be funded from his or her own purse.

(Twigg, 1997, p. 214)

Crudely, this means that some people will have to pay to be bathed at home, because they are defined as needing 'social care', while others, who have been defined as having 'health care' needs, will get the same service for nothing.

The criteria for being assessed as in need of continuing health care are very tightly drawn, so tightly that only 20,000 people qualified in England in 2005–06 (Wanless, 2006). The financial consequences of falling on one side or the other of the health/social care divide are significant.

A House of Commons Select Committee summarised the situation:

> In practice the boundary between the two services [health and social care] has shifted over time, so that the long term care responsibilities of the NHS have reduced substantially, and people who in the past would have been cared for in NHS long stay wards are now often accommodated in nursing homes. This means that responsibility for funding long term care has to a major extent been shunted from the NHS to local authorities and individual patients and their families.

(Quoted in Wanless, 2006, pp. 73–4)

Postcode lottery

Where you live: the postcode lottery

Many decisions about funding for social care are taken locally, not nationally. What you pay will depend on where you live, as well as your circumstances. You have learned already that in Manchester people assessed as being at substantial or critical risk are entitled to local authority-managed social care, and that some areas are more and some less generous than this. How much people pay towards the services they get is also decided locally. A survey in 2004 found considerable variation in how much local authorities charge users. 15% of English councils charged a maximum of £44 per week; 14% charged a maximum of £400 per week (Thompson and Mathew, 2004). This has given rise to accusations of a 'postcode lottery': that what you get depends on where you live. This may seem unfair. However, decisions are taken by locally elected councils, and it is likely that any national system would provoke similar criticisms.

Prevention or crisis management

The White Paper *Our Health, Our Care, Our Say* (DH, 2006) sets out a vision of active intervention when people's needs are only low or moderate, to ensure that people have the best quality of life possible. However, as you have seen, in practice most local authorities target people who are at critical risk if they do not get help. Age Concern, a charity which works for older people, argues that this approach is short-sighted, and likely to lead to more people entering residential care:

> What councils are doing is very short term and so we are seeing councils providing care for people with higher and higher needs whereas services should be aimed at people with lower needs.

> (Tickle, 2007, p. 29)

As ever, resources are limited, and difficult decisions have to be made about apportioning money raised through taxation. Would you vote for a party which promised better care – but told you you'd have to pay more in tax to fund it?

The aspirations for social care are to provide the conditions which will maximise choice and independence, and promote health. In practice, this is difficult to achieve in a complicated and, many say, underfunded system. The answer to the question 'Who pays for social care?' is a complex one: far more complex than the answer to 'Who pays for health care?'. Health care is, by and large, funded from national taxation. The costs of social care fall on local authorities, which make decisions about who to include, and how much to charge; and they fall on individuals according both to their means and to where they live. Whereas health care is widely regarded as a public responsibility, social care is seen by government as a mainly private responsibility, to be borne by the person who needs the care, and their family. Means testing and strict eligibility criteria target public resources at people who are at high risk and have limited personal resources. The wealthier someone is, the more likely it is that they will have to use their own money to fund care. But the system is dogged by accusations of unfairness, and its complexity can deter people from coming forward to ask for help – as the case study shows.

Key points

- Publicly provided social care services are not universal – to qualify for them people usually need to be at substantial or critical risk.

- The boundary between health and social care is difficult to draw, but hotly contested because health care is free to users, whereas social care is not.

- Long-term or continuing care is increasingly seen as social care rather than health care, meaning that the costs fall on individuals.

- Local variations can mean a 'postcode lottery' for both the quality and the costs of care.

- Although the aspiration is for services to maximise independence for care recipients and carers, in practice this is rarely achieved because of lack of resources.

3 Home care: workers and users

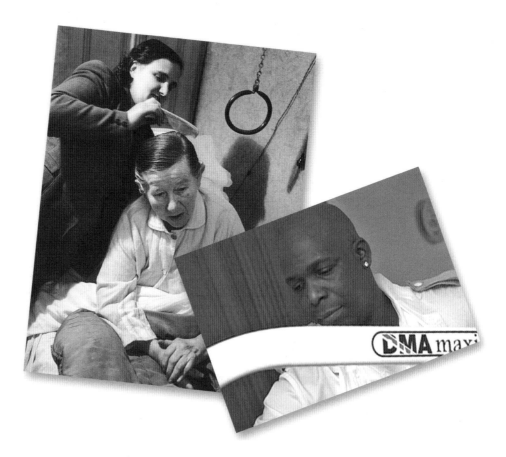

Home care workers in
1946 and 2007

You have learned about the system behind the provision of social care. In this section we turn our attention back to the front line: to the people who provide home care, and the people who receive it. If people like Angus are to be able to stay in their own homes, despite significant health problems, the workers who support them become ever more important.

3.1 Home care: what is the job?

Ann had high expectations of the difference home care would make to her life, but Angus was vehemently opposed to having anyone other than Ann take care of him. This suggests that going into someone else's home as a home care worker, when perhaps they have very mixed feelings about it, requires tact and diplomacy.

Home care is a development of what used to be the home help service which, if you are old enough, you might remember. However, with home help the job primarily comprised housework, whereas home care is far more than that.

Home care workers need a range of skills in order to work with different people. Some of their clients are seriously ill and need skilled care, including use of sophisticated equipment. Others need help only with personal care, such as washing and dressing, and domestic tasks, like shopping. The needs of yet others are primarily social. In the next activity you will see all this as you observe four very different care situations.

As you have already seen with Yetunde, one of the big challenges for home care workers is to establish the right kind of relationships with the people whose homes they enter. They have to draw the right line between being friendly and keeping people company, on the one hand, and being professional and doing their job in the time allowed in the care plan, on the other. This is a challenge for many people who work in health and social care, but it is particularly acute for people who work in home care, because their job involves going into people's homes. They are not working in their own workplace where they can be in control. Rather, they have to adapt to each person in their home. In the scenes you are about to watch, you will have a chance to consider how they manage this challenge.

In this and the next section of the unit, we will be working with a real-life case study of a care agency. Here is a brief introduction.

Somebody Cares

Somebody Cares is a privately owned and managed home care agency in Cardiff. You will meet the Managing Director, Julie Borek, in Section 4.

The case study focuses on four people who use the services of Somebody Cares, and on their care workers. They are:

- Brian Hole and his wife June, with care workers Kevin Madden and Elvis Malcolm
- Clarice Jones with care worker Liz Randall
- Aerwyn Hall with care worker Elvis Malcolm
- Lyn Smith with care worker Maria Williams (plus driver Don).

The next activity will introduce you to these people more fully.

DVD

Activity 7   The home carer's job

Allow about 45 minutes

In this activity you explore the nature of home care work by observing four care workers in action.

Go to the DVD and find Block 1, Unit 3, Activity 7.

Comment

As you have seen, being a home care worker is not straightforward. It is not about being a friend, although it is about being friendly. Workers must respect health and safety requirements, they must be clear about their responsibilities, and they must be competent to carry out quite a range of tasks. They need to manage relationships so that they can do what they need to do in the time available. Clients cannot contact them individually outside the allocated working hours.

Preserving the
boundaries

Learning skills: Working with documentary video

Previously on the DVD you have been working with case material in the
form of a fictionalised audio drama. (In Unit 2 you also had the fictionalised
case of Anwar Malik, presented through text.) However, with the case study
of the Somebody Cares agency you are working with scenes from real life.
These can seem deceptively 'ordinary' – but in fact they provide a very rich
resource. (A lot of the case material in K101 takes this 'documentary' form.)

It is quite a privilege to be able to accompany carers as they go inside
people's homes. We are seeing sensitive and personal care relationships
in action – and a great deal is 'going on' just to maintain the 'normality' of
the relationships. It is relatively easy to take an interest when things go
wrong (as you saw with the Ann and Angus drama). But when things are
going well, it can seem that it's all 'natural'. However, care relationships are
not natural. They have to be set up and maintained to provide the required
support. The appearance of naturalness is a tribute to the skills of the care
workers. So there is a lot to notice, to reflect on and to learn from in the
video scenes you have just watched. For this reason, you will be returning
to the Somebody Cares video several times in this unit.

Marking out the boundaries between work and friendship is important. Uniforms
help in this regard. As well as being practical, they are visual markers of the fact
that this is a job, not just a casual helping-out arrangement.

I wonder if you also noticed that home care workers are developing their own
specialist language. Kevin and Elvis talk about Brian being a 'double hander' –
someone who needs two workers for each shift – and Brian also uses this term to
describe himself. Workers and clients alike talk about 'morning care', 'afternoon
care' and 'evening care'.

Most jobs have their own language – or jargon, as it is sometimes called. Perhaps
yours does too. However, the special language and the uniforms do not always

protect people from finding the job quite upsetting. Liz Randall, whom you saw on the programme working with Clarice, commented to the team who recorded the DVD how hard it could be:

> I think it's hard keeping it so professional. A lot of them die in our job. The office can't contact us all, letting us know, and you might find out a couple of days later. I think regular carers obviously they're contacted. But it might be somebody who I only go to once a week, but I've been going there for twelve months or so. And you find out that they've suddenly gone into hospital, and when they come back out, well maybe in for a fortnight, two months, three months whatever ... they might not come back on my rota. And I think 'Oh I can't go' ... you can't go and see them. Unless it's down on your rota to go down and see them. So that's quite hard. Because you do get fond of them, you can't help it. Well you wouldn't be human I think, if you didn't.

Liz's reflection is a reminder that there is an emotional side to home care work for which workers may well need support. This is an issue to which you will return in Section 4 of this unit.

The service user's perspective

We now switch from the care worker's perspective to that of the service user – or client as they are referred to in our case study. Already in this unit, you have learned about some of the criticisms of home care made by people who use it. The 2006 Report by the Commission for Social Care Inspection recorded people's dissatisfaction with:

- **Inflexibility**. They would have liked more say in when carers came, what they did, and for how long.

- **Unreliability of services**. Care workers did not always come when they were expected.

- **Frequent changes of staff**. This meant that service users did not get to know the workers.

- **Poorly trained staff**. Staff did not always have the right skills or attitudes, or did not treat service users with respect.

To read a list like this gives rather a bleak picture of home care. How does this compare with the picture we get from the Somebody Cares case study?

DVD

Activity 8   Home care: the client's perspective
Allow about 30 minutes

Having examined the work of the home carers at Somebody Cares, it's time to turn the spotlight on to the experiences of the four clients and the quality of care they receive.

Go to the DVD and find Block 1, Unit 3, Activity 8.

Comment

You have seen the value of home care as a way of enabling people to live in their own homes, with a reasonable quality of life, rather than in a residential home or, in Brian's case, a hospital. You have also seen the range of ways in which care is paid for – an illustration of the 'who pays?' theme in Section 2.

From what you see on the DVD, Somebody Cares provides a service for these service users, which is of a higher standard than some of that reported in the Commission for Social Care Inspection's 2006 survey. There is some choice of care worker, some flexibility, and the fact that no one comments on reliability suggests that they can indeed rely on people arriving when they are due. Nobody comments on training either. Instead, they single out personal qualities, people they like, people who get to know how they like things done, who are friendly, who treat them as human beings. If their care workers did not display these qualities, we might expect the clients to comment on the need for training.

In this section you have considered in some depth the work of home carers, and the experiences of people who receive home care. This builds on your work in Section 1 on Ann and Angus' experiences. You have seen that home care work is about more than just being friendly and kind: it requires considerable skill to do it well. It also requires human qualities – qualities that many clients single out as being of prime importance. At the same time, it requires people to be firm about the differences between being a friend and being a care worker. Clients like Brian and June, and Lyn recognise this too. Some clients, however, like Aerwyn, like to minimise the difference. In Aerwyn's case, the job is to be a friend, albeit only for the time the carer is with him. It is also a job which makes significant emotional demands on workers who have to manage relationships with people who are ill or vulnerable.

Meeting people's needs in ways that are both professional and friendly, and flexible and reliable is not straightforward. It is, however, a very important responsibility. How would Clarice manage if for any reason Liz or another worker was unable to come? She might be in considerable difficulty and distress. To run a care agency that can provide the flexibility and, at the same time, the reliability of service that clients want is a significant challenge. This is the topic of the next section.

Key points

- Home care workers provide a vital service in enabling people to stay in their own homes when they have care needs.

- Home care workers work to a care plan which determines what they do for each client.

- Home care workers need to manage relationships with clients so that there are clear boundaries between being friendly and being 'a friend'. At times this makes considerable emotional demands.

- Personal qualities are important, but not enough. Home carers need technical skills too.

- People value home care that is reliable and flexible, and which is delivered with kindness and with respect for them as individuals.

4 This caring business

In this section you continue to consider the work of Somebody Cares, but this time from a business perspective. Somebody Cares is a business, there to make money as well as provide a service.

Somebody Cares, like other providers of home care services in England, Wales and Northern Ireland (but not Scotland), is 'commissioned' by publicly funded bodies, usually the local authority, to provide services. In the case of Somebody Cares, most of its funding comes from Cardiff Social Services. As the commissioner, Cardiff Social Services retains responsibility for making sure the agency delivers the services it has promised, and to the quality that has been specified. The agency employs, manages and pays the staff.

To put it another way, in home care there are three major players:

- **Commissioners**. These are the agencies which contract and pay for services. Their budgets come from local or national taxes and they spend them on commissioning services for people eligible for help. Commissioners are responsible not only for purchasing the services, but also for making sure the service is delivered as specified in the contract. Commissioners of social care are public sector bodies, variously known as adult social care, social services, community care, social work departments, primary care trusts, health boards.

- **Providers**. These are either private profit-making companies like Somebody Cares, or not-for-profit voluntary organisations. They contract with commissioners to provide services for a given period of time and at an agreed price. They employ and manage the staff.

- **Clients or service users**. These are the people who use the services, some of whom (like Clarice and Lyn on the DVD) contribute financially to the costs, but who (usually) do not pay directly for the services.

In the rest of this section you will consider how this system works, using Somebody Cares as an example. You will be asked to think about this in two ways:

- care as a business
- managing for quality.

Facts and figures about Somebody Cares

The company was founded in 2002. It grew steadily from four to forty care workers in four years. It had, at the time of the recording (in 2007), about 160 clients, the majority on contracts from local councils, with some paying privately for services. It had excellent reports in 2006 and 2007 from the Care Standards Inspectorate for Wales (now the Care and Social Services Inspectorate Wales; see, for example, CSSIW, 2007). The company is registered with the Care Council and with several of the local authorities in the Cardiff area.

(Details provided by Julie Borek, Managing Director)

DVD

Activity 9   Care as a business

Allow about 20 minutes

You can now listen to Julie Borek, Managing Director of Somebody Cares, talking about the challenges of running a home care business.

Go to the DVD and find Block 1, Unit 3, Activity 9.

Comment

You have heard what a complex task it is to manage a care business. You have also heard that although there is plenty of business – a lot of people needing care services – staffing is the critical issue. Julie has to ensure that the people served by her agency are covered, even when bad weather makes travelling difficult. If the carer does not arrive, some users like Clarice will be in serious discomfort, while others may be at considerable risk.

You know from Section 3 that Somebody Cares is popular with its service users. It seems to have managed to avoid some of the criticisms that users of home care have expressed. How has this been achieved?

DVD

Activity 10   Managing for quality

Allow about 20 minutes

In our interview with Julie we were keen to find out what was involved in managing for quality. What did she do that makes her company popular? You can now hear her explain some of the ingredients of her success.

Go to the DVD and find Block 1, Unit 3, Activity 10.

Comment

Julie Borek is able to point to a variety of measures put in place to ensure that the staff of Somebody Cares are fully trained and prepared for their work. Equally important, monitoring and spot checks are carried out to ensure that staff are aware of how well they are performing their duties.

Somebody Cares home care worker

Reader

Learning skills: Using 'grids' to make notes

You have now done several exercises with the video material about Somebody Cares, each of which required you to fill in a table or grid. This is a very important type of activity when you are studying. 'Analysing' issues is a key part of university-level understanding. What a grid does is help you to ask a series of questions in a systematic way, which is the essence of analysis. It also enables you to set out your answers systematically. In the activity you have just done, you were able to look at several different aspects of quality assurance and to ask the same two questions of each: 'What does Somebody Cares do?' and 'How does doing this help with quality of care?' Filling in the grid enabled you to turn the flow of talk from Julie Borek into a systematic analysis of what the agency says it does about quality assurance. It isn't a hugely detailed analysis, but it doesn't need to be. It serves the purpose of focusing your attention on the variety of different types of procedure that need to be put in place, and why.

The same purposes are served by the grids you completed earlier. And this 'grid technique' is one you can use for yourself in your own note taking – when you are provided with less guidance on how to view a DVD track or read a chapter. To give yourself a few more ideas about how you might do this, take a look at Section 6.4.1 of *The Good Study Guide* (pages 148–50). Read from the start of the section.

Judging from our interviews with them, the staff of Somebody Cares seem to appreciate the care their employer takes. Care worker Kevin Madden compares Somebody Cares favourably with other employers:

> Well Somebody Cares I find as a company is one of the main companies what do put actual training in front of you. The selection is there for you. At the end of the day, they do make sure all the training is available and everyone does the training. There's a lot of companies out there, what don't. They give you a video tape to watch, and that's your training, as far as they're concerned. But Somebody Cares at the end of the day, you do get a certificate. And to say that you've done all your training. That's the great pleasure you get working for a good company as that.

From all the evidence we have, then, from the workers, the clients and the Care Standards Inspectorate for Wales/CSSIW, which gave Somebody Cares 'excellent' reviews in two consecutive years, this is one of the better companies working in the sector. Nevertheless, along with other agencies contracted to provide care, Somebody Cares does face challenges and constraints in providing quality. Your final activity in this section asks you to consider these.

DVD

Activity 11   Challenges to maintaining high-quality care
Allow about 20 minutes

Your last visit to Somebody Cares is to hear Julie Borek again, this time talking about various challenges to maintaining the quality of the care the agency provides.

Go to the DVD and find Block 1, Unit 3, Activity 11.

Comment

As you have heard, maintaining high standards in home care services is very challenging. It requires a well-thought out, vigorous and determined approach.

Even for a well-run company like Somebody Cares, it can be a struggle to maintain high-quality home care services in the face of cost constraints and the challenges of managing staff. Home care users want flexibility. They would like their care delivered by the person they choose, when and how they want it, but this is a huge challenge when there are 160 people to look after. The fact that agencies have to serve many people within a budget set by the local authority means that individuals cannot always determine who their carer is, the time they arrive or what they do on a given day.

In this section you have considered the provision of home care from the point of view of the agency which provides it. You have learned about the role of the commissioner (usually the local authority) which contracts with Somebody Cares to provide services to individuals, according to an agreed care plan. You have considered what is required to provide a high-quality service which ensures that staff are well trained and supported, that monitoring of their performance is carried out, and that there are opportunities for users to complain. And you have pondered the challenges of providing high-quality care given the complexity of staff allocation to 160 people, and the cost constraints set by the commissioner. In the light of this, it is perhaps unsurprising that surveys, such as the one conducted by the Commission for Social Care Inspection in England in 2006, have uncovered considerable dissatisfaction with home care on the part of the people who use it. Even the best run companies, of which Somebody Cares is undoubtedly one, will have difficulties in meeting everyone's expectations while ensuring health and safety for the workforce, and remaining within budget.

In the final section of this unit you will consider Direct Payments, another approach to providing care services which, some argue, is a way of avoiding some of these issues.

Key points

- Providers of home care are commissioned by public bodies, usually local authorities.
- Recruitment, management and training of well-motivated staff is core to the provision of high-quality home care.
- However well managed, home care agencies struggle to provide the care their clients want and need in the context of cost constraints set by commissioners and managing competing demands from large numbers of clients.

Learning skills: Study shock

You are nearing the end of your third K101 unit – how are you coping? Have you ever done as much reading as you have in the last three weeks? Does it feel like a tidal wave washing over you? Many people find the first impact of OU study a bit unnerving. When else in adult life are you expected to think so hard and concentrate for so long – and in your leisure time too? Can you keep this up? Be reassured that most people do begin to get into the swing of things after a few weeks. You should eventually find a 'second wind'. Until you do, the main thing is just to take what you can from each unit, and keep moving on to the next one at the end of the week. It's *your* course. Don't let it get you down! Whenever you do feel that things are getting a bit much, why not go into one of the online forums and ask whether anyone else is feeling the same? Sharing a few ideas about how to keep things in proportion is often an excellent way of getting your momentum back.

The Block 1 skills week

Next week brings a break in the flow, when you switch to skills work instead. You also have time set aside for your assignment. Whatever else you might miss, try not to fall behind with the assignment. Indeed, if you haven't done so already, have a look at the essay titles now, or when you've finished this unit. Then you can start mulling over ideas before getting down to serious work on it next week. Don't wait until the last minute to look, because essays often take longer than you think. Make sure you allow time to do yourself justice.

5 Providing home care: an alternative model

In this final section of Unit 3, you will be considering an alternative model of providing home care to that experienced by Angus and Ann and carried out by home carers like Yetunde, and that provided by Somebody Cares in Cardiff. This alternative is Direct Payments, where the user employs his or her own personal assistant.

5.1 Users' criticisms of home care

As you know, one of the main criticisms users have of home care provided by agencies is that they, the users, are not in charge. They may pay towards the costs, but that money goes back to the commissioner, not directly to the home carer. The agency determines the rotas, decides which carer will work with which client on a given day, and, although the user may complain, as many do, it is not easy either for the agency to change its practices, or for the individual home carers to offer a better service than they are mandated to offer through the care plan, the rota, and the demands of other clients.

Although there is good practice – examples of which you have encountered in the unit – there is no way to guarantee that. Phil Cotterell, a researcher who interviewed users of home care, remarks that 'positive experiences primarily concerned individual workers who had good personal skills and who knew the client' (Cotterell, 2007, p. 30). However, this is far from guaranteed by the system, and there is extensive evidence that users are often dissatisfied (CSCI, 2006).

The failings are graphically illustrated in the following account by Simon Heng:

> … I need help with every physical task, including getting out of bed. A few days ago, the carer who usually gets me ready in the morning needed to go on a training course, and a local agency provided a replacement.

> I'm not the quickest self-starter in the morning, and certainly not very chatty … Soon after starting, she commented: 'Not very talkative, are we?'

> … The 'we' grated a little, but I didn't feel like picking a fight, firstly because I was lying in bed – and feeling rather vulnerable, as most people would when naked in a room with a fully clothed stranger – and secondly because I hadn't got all my wits about me.

> The breaking point came later, when she was giving me some toast. I could just about bear it when she opened and closed her mouth with every mouthful that I took, but it was too much when she decided to provide a running commentary: 'Ooh, that was a BIG bite!'

> […]

> As we were finishing, she said 'I suppose you're going to be watching television for the rest of the day? Maybe you might go down to the shops?'

(Heng, 2005)

5.2 Putting the user in charge: Direct Payments

If part of the problem in providing the type of home care people want is that the user does not employ or pay the carer, then it might work if that were changed, putting the user in charge directly. This is a system called Direct Payments, a model which puts the user, client or patient in the driving seat, by giving him or her the cash to spend on meeting assessed needs.

Direct Payments and Individual Budgets

A Direct Payment is a cash payment made by a local authority to a person assessed as needing certain services, such as home care, so that they can buy services for themselves. An individual then uses the payment to meet their assessed support needs, instead of the local authority providing or buying services on their behalf. When the Direct Payment has been agreed, an amount will be paid into the individual's bank or building society account each month and this must be used by them to meet their assessed needs. People can receive mixed packages of support, with a Direct Payment and some directly provided services (www.dh.gov.uk). Direct Payments are intended to:

> Promote independence, choice and inclusion … to give recipients control over their own life by providing an alternative to social care services provided by a local authority.

> (DH, 2003, pp. 3–4)

Direct Payments apply in all four UK countries, although there are some differences among the people who are eligible to receive them.

Most people who use Direct Payments use the cash to buy personal assistance with managing their daily lives. The term 'personal assistant' is used to describe the job because it often involves more than help with managing personal care. (Details provided by Jan Leece.)

You may also encounter Individual Budgets and In Control schemes (www.in-control.org.uk). These are essentially similar to Direct Payments in that they also give the service user control over the funding so that they can make choices about the type of support they need, and how it is provided.

Direct Payments have been in use in the UK since 1997, although their take-up has been slow. People who have used them, however, have on the whole been very satisfied, as you will discover in the next activity.

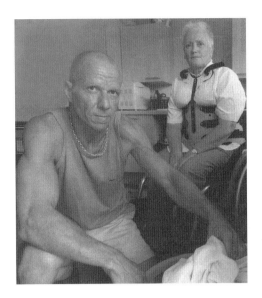

People who use Direct Payments can select their own personal assistants

Reader

Activity 12   Users' experiences of Direct Payments

Allow about 45 minutes

Read Chapter 8, Users' experience of direct payments' by Tim Stainton and Steve Boyce in the Reader (pages 65–72). Then make some notes in response to the questions below.

(a) What benefits were described by people who used Direct Payments?

(b) What drawbacks were mentioned?

(c) In this study, did Direct Payments appear to have addressed the difficulties with home care services identified by the CSCI? That is:

- frequent changes of staff, with no opportunity for the carer to get to know the client, and vice versa

- lack of flexibility to respond to individual needs

- not enough time to do what the person needs

- workers with inadequate training

- failure to treat people with respect.

(d) To what extent do you think Direct Payments met Maslow's 'higher-order needs', as discussed in Section 1 of this unit?

Comment

(a) **Benefits of Direct Payments**. These were described as considerable. The people who used Direct Payments described more flexibility; being able to come and go more freely; familiarity with the personal assistant; empathy and understanding; companionship; control; confidence; not having to explain needs each time a new person appeared.

(b) **Drawbacks**. Not many were mentioned, although someone commented that keeping the boundary between work and friendship was tricky. This is, of course, particularly acute where the personal assistant is an existing friend, or a family member, as was often the case.

(c) **Problems identified by the CSCI**. The people in this study seemed to think that most of the problems identified by the CSCI had been dealt with. They got to know their personal assistant; knew who to expect; could decide how the time was used and when they needed help; they felt respected. Training was the one area which Direct Payments didn't seem to address, although the people in this study did not seem unduly bothered about that.

(d) **Meeting 'higher-order needs'**. The article gives clear signs that personal assistants did support these users with what Maslow called 'higher-order needs': for social activities, love and friendship; for self-respect and recognition by others; and for their development and growth. The users were able to take more responsibility for their own lives. One mentioned doing a computer course, another how the personal assistants were able to manage even though it had been a difficult year health-wise; yet another that the personal assistant was able to accompany them to distant specialist outpatient appointments. It seems likely that had agency care workers been employed, they almost certainly would not have worked in such a way as to make it possible to meet people's needs for opportunities to grow and develop through doing courses and getting back to work.

Direct Payments do seem to offer many advantages over the system you learned about in Sections 1 to 4 of this unit. But in the study you have just read, there were some unanswered questions.

The first set of questions relates to the personal assistants. Did they enjoy the work? How well were they paid? Did they get training? Who looks after their interests? What did the Direct Payments role do to existing relationships? What happens if personal assistants fall ill or decide to move on?

The second question concerns the users. Are these users typical of all sorts of people who need care? They seem to be younger adults, perhaps physically rather than mentally disabled, and more able to directly manage someone else's work.

The Direct Payments model has had a very good press, and you can see why after considering the article. But there remain outstanding questions as to whether it can be the main answer to the challenge of providing good-quality care services. Some of these questions relate to the staffing side of the Direct Payments model, others to its suitability for all care users.

5.3 The personal assistant role

In Section 3 of this unit you considered the home carer's role in some detail. Now it is time to turn attention to the role of the personal assistant.

Activity 13   Home carers and personal assistants: comparing the jobs

Allow about 20 minutes

Use the table below to jot down some thoughts on the pros and cons of being a home carer employed by an agency versus a personal assistant employed directly by a service user. There won't be clear-cut answers in every case: just use what you have studied to set down your thoughts.

	Home carer	Personal assistant
Terms and conditions of work		
Training opportunities		
Career prospects		
Choice of clients		
Relationship with client		
Amount of personal risk associated with the job		
Job satisfaction		

Comment

Here are my thoughts on the two jobs.

	Home carer	Personal assistant
Terms and conditions of work	Involves unsocial hours, and the need to be flexible	Involves unsocial hours, and the need to be flexible
Training opportunities	Varies, but these ought to be available (in the way they are for staff at Somebody Cares)	Probably none in a formal sense
Career prospects	Limited, but possibility of attaining supervisory or managerial roles	None
Choice of clients	Very limited	Considerable
Relationship with client	Will vary, but formally constrained by care plan, employer's regulations and health and safety considerations	Personally negotiated, but there may well be issues associated with maintaining a boundary between work and friendship
Amount of personal risk associated with the job	Vulnerable as they work alone, often in the homes of people they do not know	Limited, although there may be some if the relationship with the employer goes wrong
Job satisfaction	Depends on the clients and the way the job is managed by the agency	Likely to be considerable if they get on with the person who employs them

If your assessment agreed with mine, you will have concluded that the personal assistant role probably has more inherent satisfaction than that of the home carer. Personal assistants have more choice about whom they work with, and may well have more choice over what they do. Research by Jan Leece, which compared home care work with personal assistant work in Staffordshire, found that personal assistants had more job satisfaction and less stress than home carers. One personal assistant commented:

> I don't class it as a job because I forget, I'm just here. If I didn't come round she'd miss me … I do enjoy what I'm doing. It suits me it suits my kids it suits her and it suits her kids … I wouldn't want to be stuck in an office all day.
>
> (Leece, 2006, p. 197)

Another said:

> It is a really comfortable job, hence the fact that I've been here just over five years and we get on really well.
>
> (Leece, 2006, p. 197)

However, Leece also found that:

- The pay of personal assistants was markedly poorer than that of home care workers.

- Personal assistants lack any formal opportunities for promotion, training or progression in their careers.

- Seven of the eight personal assistants she interviewed worked more than the time they were paid for, some substantially more.

- They are vulnerable if the one-to-one relationship goes wrong.

She sums up her findings thus:

> The direct payments relationship appears in a positive light when compared to home care work … The new 'professional', impersonal role of the home care worker in providing task-based support may essentially be less satisfying and more stressful for some workers than the informal direct payments relationship. However, this does not justify the present system, which results in direct payments users having to offer low pay and poor terms of employment to their personal assistants.
>
> (Leece, 2006, pp. 201–2)

5.4 Suitability for all?

The second unanswered question was whether Direct Payments would work for everybody who needs support with daily living. The users in the study you read were younger and more articulate than many people who need care. How might Angus have managed with a personal assistant? It might have changed his life, but he might have found the responsibility of recruiting, managing and paying someone quite onerous.

Tom Shakespeare, a disabled academic, argues that Direct Payments are most suitable for people with permanent impairments, and for people with long-term illnesses, and are less likely to be a solution for babies and children, people who have severe learning disabilities, or mental health problems, and older, frail people or people with dementia (Shakespeare, 2006, p. 136).

As Direct Payments have become more common, so more formal arrangements to support people to manage them successfully are emerging. This in itself raises questions about whether personal assistants need to be bound by legislation designed to protect users from abuse, such as Criminal Records Bureau checks (Scourfield, 2005). At the time I wrote this (in 2007), these measures were being vigorously resisted by people who use Direct Payments. They argued that their freedom in choosing a personal assistant would be undermined, and the nature of the support would become more like existing home care services. However, as more people use the Direct Payments model, the pressures to regulate personal assistants, in the interests of protecting people, are likely to increase.

In this section you have been considering who is in charge in the relationship between a paid care worker and the client/service user/patient. The concept you have been asked to use to consider this has been the idea of Direct Payments, making the person who uses the service the employer who actually chooses the worker (a personal assistant) and pays their wages. This does seem to change the relationship between user and worker quite considerably, giving the user more power to decide who they want to employ, what they want them to do, and when they want them to do it. There are advantages for the workers, too, because the job offers less stress and more personal satisfaction than the job of home carer. But there are drawbacks, particularly in terms of the pay and conditions on offer to people who work in the personal assistant role.

Key points

- Although individual workers often give excellent service, there have been many criticisms of home care delivered by agencies.

- Direct Payments, in which people who use services hold the money and choose and pay their own personal assistants, are a way of changing the power relationship between users and workers in home care.

- People who have used Direct Payments report much greater satisfaction than people who use more traditional home care services. Workers also report greater satisfaction, and less stress.

- Personal assistants are low paid and lack opportunities for training and career progression.

- Direct Payments may be more suitable for some groups of service users than for others.

Conclusion

In this unit you have considered the role that home care plays in supporting people who have care needs. The unit has focused on care for older adults because they are the main users of social care services. The policy intention is that people should be supported in their own homes as far as possible, even when they are quite ill and frail. (You have met several such people in this unit.) However, the system is under strain and people find it hard to understand how it works, who is eligible and how it is paid for. It has given rise to a new set of workers, home carers and personal assistants, whose job is quite a delicate balance between professionalism and friendliness. The system works well for many users and carers, but, as you have learned, there are some difficulties.

The unit began with the Ann and Angus case study, following them as they entered the roles of being receivers of social care. In Section 2, you then learned about the system that local authorities use in deciding where to target their resources, and the quite intricate way in which it is paid for; and you have noted the tension between policy aspirations, which seek to maximise choice and independence, and the reality on the ground, where scarce resources have to be rationed to those at most risk. In Section 3, you examined how home care workers carry out their job, from the perspectives of both workers and users. Then, in Section 4, you considered the challenges of managing a home care business, particularly the importance of recruiting, training and managing high-quality staff, and some of the difficulties of providing what clients want in the face of limited financial resources and competing demands. Finally, you examined another approach to providing care, Direct Payments: one of a range of ways of putting the money in the hands of the person who needs care, and enabling them to choose and direct their personal assistants. This appears to offer many advantages, both to workers and to users, but there remain reservations about the dangers of exploiting the goodwill of people who work in this role.

Learning skills: Reading to learn

You have done three weeks' worth of intensive reading now and we hope you have found it stimulating and informative. But how effective a reader do you feel you are? Reading takes up by far the largest part of your studies, so it is very important to think about what you are supposed to be achieving from it, and whether you are going about it the best way.

To help you develop your reading technique, your last task for this week is to read Chapter 5 of *The Good Study Guide*. You will find that it asks you to read a three-page article about whether living in our kind of society makes us happy. The author of the article, Richard Layard, has made a big impact with his writing on this subject and has been an adviser to the Government on how to improve happiness levels in society. This short extract from a longer article gives you a flavour of his line of thinking. It's not directly on the topic of 'care', but it's very relevant. It's important to do the initial reading exercise properly so that the rest of the chapter works for you – and also because the rest of the book keeps referring back to the article. Chapter 5 will give you plenty to think about and should take you about two hours to work through. You will find it is an excellent time investment.

Reader

Read Chapter 5 of *The Good Study Guide* (pages 101–28), working on the activities as you come to them.

End-of-unit checklist

Now that you have reached the end of this unit, you should find you are able to:

- describe home care and how it is funded and provided
- understand the changes that families go through when they enter the social care system
- describe the work of a home carer and the extent to which they are able to respond to the needs of the people they work for
- discuss social care as a business
- debate the advantages and disadvantages of Direct Payments as a way of providing care.

References

Butler, P. (2007) 'Need for a new package deal?', *Guardian Society*, 10 January, p. 3; also available online at www.guardian.co.uk/society/2007/jan/10/socialcare.longtermcare (Accessed 19 December 2007).

Care and Social Services Inspectorate Wales (CSSIW) (2007) [online], www.csiw.wales.gov.uk/dataviewer/details.asp?code=11949&searchtext=&postcode=&settings=&authority=&region=c&results=true&providers= (Accessed 26 February 2008)

CarenapE (1999) *Care Needs Assessment Package for the Elderly*, Version 3, August 1999, Crown copyright.

College of Occupational Therapists (2006) *Minor Adaptations with Delay*, London, College of Occupational Therapists.

Commission for Social Care Inspection (CSCI) (2006) *Time to Care? An Overview of Home Care Services for Older People in England*, London, Commission for Social Care Inspection; also available online at www.csci.org.uk/professional/about_csci/publications/view.aspx?csci=1751 (Accessed 19 December 2007).

Cotterell, P. (2007) 'How home care can help', *Community Care*, 18–24 January, pp. 30–1.

Department of Health (DH) (2003) *Direct Payments Guidance: Community Care Services for Carers and Children's Services (Direct Payments) Guidance, England 2003*, London, Department of Health.

Department of Health (DH) (2006) *Our Health, Our Care, Our Say: A New Direction for Community Services*, Norwich, The Stationery Office.

Foster, M., Harris, J., Jackson, K., Morgan, H. and Glendinning, C. (2007) 'Personalised social care for adults with disabilities: a problematic concept for front line practitioners', *Health and Social Care in the Community*, vol. 14, no. 2, pp. 125–35.

Heng, S. (2005) 'The Simon Heng column', *Community Care*, 24–30 November [online], www.communitycare.co.uk/Articles/2005/11/24/51909/the-simon-heng-column.html (Accessed 28 February 2008).

Leece, J. (2006) '"It's not like being at work": a study to investigate stress and job satisfaction in employees of direct payments users' in Leece, J. and Bornat, J. (eds) *Developments in Direct Payments*, Bristol, The Policy Press.

Maslow, A. (1970) *Motivation and Personality*, London, Harper & Row.

Morris, J. (2004) 'Independent living and community care: a disempowering framework', *Disability and Society*, vol. 19, no. 5, pp. 427–42.

Scottish Executive (2007) *Evaluation of the Operation and Impact of Free Personal Care*, Edinburgh, Blackwell; also available online at www.scotland.gov.uk/Publications/2007/02/27143831/20 (Accessed 5 April 2008).

Scourfield, P. (2005) 'Implementing the Community Care (Direct Payments) Act', *Journal of Social Policy*, vol. 34, no. 3, pp. 469–88.

Shakespeare, T. (2006) *Disability Rights and Wrongs*, London, Routledge.

Thompson, P. and Mathew, D. (2004) *Fair Enough? Research on the Implementation of the Department of Health's Guidance on Fairer Charging Policies for Home Care and other Non Residential Social Services*, London, Age Concern.

Tickle, L. (2007) 'The great home care divide', *Community Care*, 19–25 April, p. 29.

Twigg, J. (1997) 'Deconstructing the social bath: help with bathing at home for older and disabled people', *Journal of Social Policy*, vol. 26, no. 2, pp. 211–32.

Wanless, D. (2006) *Securing Good Care for Older People: Taking a Long-term View*, London, King's Fund.

Websites

www.dh.gov.uk (Accessed 26 February 2008).

www.dwp.gov.uk (Accessed 26 February 2008).

www.in-control.org.uk (Accessed 26 February 2008).

www.welfarerights.net (Accessed 26 February 2008).

Unit 4

Developing care relationships

Prepared for the course team by Andrew Northedge

Contents

Introduction

You have reached the final week of Block 1 and it is time for a change. The last unit of each K101 block is a 'skills' unit. Instead of the intensive reading you have been doing, the focus of the skills units is on activities. These units are shorter than the others. Each unit should take about six hours to complete, which will leave time for your end-of-block assignment.

Each end-of-block skills unit focuses on three types of skill:

- care skills
- working with numbers
- learning skills, especially writing skills.

Care skills

Care skills are the main focus of all the skills units, but the emphasis is on a different aspect of care skills in each. Unit 4 focuses on the skills of developing good care relationships. There is some reading at first, to provide a context for the skills activities throughout K101, but most of the real care skills work is on the DVD.

Working with numbers

The skills units also include a short section to help develop your skills in reading tables and charts. In each unit you will look at one or two tables and charts to explore what the numbers can tell you, by working your way through some straightforward activities. The number skills work is all on the DVD.

Learning skills

One of the most important elements of K101 is developing your learning skills, in particular writing skills, which are so important to success in your studies. Writing is seldom simple and there are several aspects to gaining control of the writing process and learning to write well. In each block, just before you start work on your assignment, you will find some reading and a few activities to help you develop another facet of your writing skills. Often there is also some discussion of other learning skills, to help you reflect on the progress you are making and plan new strategies.

Are you taking the IVR?

If you are studying K101 as part of the Integrated Vocational Route (IVR), don't forget to check your VQ Candidate Handbook to see which Unit 4 activities contribute to your electronic portfolio.

1 Care skills: developing care relationships

Care always involves a relationship between the person receiving care and the person providing care. Moreover, the quality of that relationship directly affects the quality of the care received, as well as the experience of receiving care. You have already learned a lot about this in your study of Block 1, as well as about the stresses and strains of care relationships.

1.1 The demands of care relationships

Back in Unit 1, you heard how Angus received care and support from his daughter Ann. Their care relationship developed out of a very long established family relationship. Nevertheless, as Angus' needs became greater, they had to establish new ways of relating to each other, and this was stressful and demanding for both of them.

Similarly, in Unit 2 you read about the tensions Anwar experienced on his first visit to the doctor's surgery, and about the sometimes ineffective communication between him and Nurse Richards, as well as his difficulties in relating to the ward staff when he first arrived in hospital.

Then in Unit 3, you read about the relationships that need to be established when carers work in people's homes. When Yetunde arrived in Ann and Angus' home there were new tensions in the family. You saw how important it was that Yetunde took responsibility for managing her relationships with Angus and Ann – explaining to them what she was and was not allowed to do – even though this was not what Ann wanted to hear at the time. Also, she remained calm when Angus complained about things, or presumed to make up his own name for her. And she took pains to establish good relations with other members of the family, as when she helped Zoe to get closer to her grandfather. Later, you saw real care relationships in action, as you watched home care workers from the Somebody Cares agency working with their clients. You also heard the views of both clients and care workers on the importance of the care relationship.

A special kind of relationship

To set up a care relationship that works well requires skill. Care relationships are never just a matter of 'doing what comes naturally'. For one thing, a carer is expected to provide exactly the same quality of care regardless of whether the person receiving the care is someone they would like in other walks of life. Also, unlike the kind of 'normal' relationships where you might have fallings out and reconciliations, the care relationship has to continue in a calm and consistent way, whatever upsets occur. In other words, a care relationship has to be specially 'constructed'. You are not simply relating to someone according to your personal inclination. You have a particular kind of role to play. Understanding the nature of the caring role and learning how to play it is a key part of becoming a skilled carer.

Care relationships are not ordinary. Care may often include activities which cross the normal boundaries of what goes on in relationships between people. For example, what is known as intimate care – washing, bathing, toileting and dressing – involves carers, or care workers, seeing and touching parts of the body which are normally private. So, care relationships have to be developed in ways that allow these activities to be undertaken without causing embarrassment or undermining dignity. Care can also involve knowing things about a person that they might normally keep to themselves. Consequently, a care relationship involves trust – trust that the carer will be respectful in crossing boundaries, will not give personal information to others and will not exploit the care situation in any way.

Shortly, you will be looking at how this kind of trust can be developed in care relationships, as well as at other aspects of the special kind of relationship that care requires. But first we ask, if care relationships are indeed special, how can the right kinds of approach be established in the millions of care relationships across the UK?

1.2 Achieving competent care practice

In official language, a skilled carer is someone who is 'competent' in care practice. But what does it take to be considered a competent care worker? In recent decades, great strides have been made in defining the basic skills of care work.

Learning skills: Reading formal documentation and background information

In this section of Unit 4 there are a number of quotations from formal documents. Please note that *it isn't necessary to read all the details closely and remember them*. The point of including the quotations is to give you a sense of the way skills are specified. It's the kind of 'reference' material you would scan through to check up on something you wanted to know. For now, you need only skim through quite quickly to pick up the general idea. Certainly don't worry about trying to remember things. You can always come back here to look things up.

It is important to be able to change your speed and style of reading to suit the kind of material and your purpose in reading it. In Section 1 the main thing is to end up being aware of *the five principles of care practice*, which appear in the box at the start of Section 1.3, and to have a sense of where the principles come from and why they are important.

Defining standards

National Occupational Standards have been defined to cover all types of health and social care work. These standards provide the basis for National Vocational Qualifications in Health and Social Care (known as NVQs or, in Scotland, SVQs). Responsibility for defining the standards lies with Sector Skills Councils. In 2007 these included: Skills for Health (www.skillsforhealth.org.uk), which has UK-wide responsibility, along with Skills for Care (responsible for England; www.skillsforcare.org.uk/), Scottish Social Services Council (www.sssc.uk.com/Homepage.htm), Northern Ireland Social Care Council (www.niscc.info) and the Care Council for Wales (www.ccwales.org.uk).

Here is how Skills for Care describes its work:

Who we are and what we do

National

Working in consultation with carers, employers and service users, Skills for Care aims to modernise adult social care in England, by ensuring qualifications and standards continually adapt to meet the changing needs of people who use care services.

We do this by:

- Developing national standards and a qualification framework for our sector
- Collecting skills data and researching issues affecting carers and people who use care services
- Creating a national workforce development strategy for all sectors
- Building employer-led regional support networks to liaise with health, local government and education at local, regional and national level.

Regional

Skills for Care regional committees contribute to the improvement of social care and social work through workforce development within their particular region of the country. Each regional committee reflects the make-up of the national Skills for Care board, with a majority of members drawn from networks of independent and statutory sector employers. Other members are service users and carers, staff groups and training interests.

(Skills for Care, undated)

The National Occupational Standards are divided into sets of competences. Every competence is then broken down in detail to describe the precise skills and knowledge a person is expected to be able to demonstrate in order to have achieved that competence. These detailed statements, taken together, amount to an 'official' definition of what good care practice is.

Variations in specification details

National variations

In this section of the unit you will see various quotations from National Occupational Standards. These standards are the responsibility of different bodies in the different UK nations. To avoid complications, all the quotations here are from the English version, available at the Skills for Care website at www.topssengland.net. However, the standards underpinning, for example, Scottish Vocational Qualifications are quite similar. The point here is just to get a flavour of the way care skills are specified. If you wanted to make comparisons with the Scottish versions, you could follow this up through the Scottish Qualifications Authority (SQA) website at www.sqa.org.uk.

Codes of practice

Defining standards is only part of it. Maintaining high standards of care practice also involves making sure that the right kind of people are employed, training them, creating the right conditions for them to work in, providing the right support and having appropriate procedures for checking that care is carried out to the required standards. All these are the responsibility not of care workers, but of their employers. And above the employers, standards are ultimately overseen by councils.

For social care, the councils have drawn up broad codes of practice. (For health care there are more specific codes covering various aspects of practice, such as confidentiality, prevention and control of health-care-associated infection, and mental health.) In recognition that standards of care are the responsibility of both care workers *and* their employers, two matching codes of practice have been developed:

> The Code of Practice for Employers of Social Care Workers sets down the responsibilities of employers in the regulation of social care workers.
>
> [...]
>
> The Code of Practice for Social Care Workers is a list of statements that describe the standards of professional conduct and practice required of social care workers as they go about their daily work.
>
> (General Social Care Council, 2002, pp. 2, 3)

These codes of practice are published by the General Social Care Council, which has responsibility for England, but they were developed in collaboration with other national care councils:

> The General Social Care Council began its work on 1 October 2001, at the same time as the Northern Ireland Social Care Council, the Scottish Social Services Council, and the Care Council for Wales. The Councils have a duty to develop codes of practice and have worked together in developing these codes as part of their contribution to raising standards in social care services.
>
> (General Social Care Council, 2002, p. 2)

The Code of Practice for Employers of Social Care Workers states that:

> To meet their responsibilities in relation to regulating the social care workforce, social care employers must:
>
> • Make sure people are suitable to enter the workforce and understand their roles and responsibilities;
>
> • Have written policies and procedures in place to enable social care workers to meet the General Social Care Council (GSCC) Code of Practice for Social Care Workers;

- Provide training and development opportunities to enable social care workers to strengthen and develop their skills and knowledge;
- Put in place and implement written policies and procedures to deal with dangerous, discriminatory or exploitative behaviour and practice; and
- Promote the GSCC's codes of practice to social care workers, service users and carers and co-operate with the GSCC's proceedings.

(General Social Care Council, 2002, p. 4)

So, while our emphasis in this unit is on exploring the skills shown by care workers, it is important to keep in mind that the quality of their practice is also a reflection of the policies and practices of their employers – the training they have been given, along with the guidelines, paper work, supervision and support.

Developing competent practice

We have seen that there are extensively defined standards of competence and also codes of practice, but what does it take to become competent in caring? According to National Occupational Standards:

Competent practice is a combination of the application of skills and knowledge informed by values and ethics.

(Skills for Care, 2005a, p. 6)

Skills are what Unit 4 is about, but what is meant here by knowledge, values and ethics?

Knowledge

You have covered a lot of knowledge in the first three units of Block 1 that will help to underpin practice in care settings:

- **Knowledge about *theories and ideas.*** For example, Parson's concept of the 'sick role', or the debate about the influence of the biomedical and social models of health care; and ideas such as 'networks of family care' and about the ways in which families have changed over time; or understanding the boundary between health care and social care and its significance in terms of how care is paid for

- **Knowledge about *policy.*** For example, that social care resources are allocated through assessments of need and risk, that local authorities commission home care from agencies, or the proposed shift in the balance of health care from hospital to community and from paternalistic relationships to partnerships

- **Knowledge about *practice.*** For example, the sort of support informal carers might need, how staff in hospitals work together, or how home care assistants actually relate to clients.

Values and ethics

You have also seen, through your work with the case studies, the kind of *values* that are appropriate to working in care. These are values such as respect, equality, justice, empowerment and protection from harm. Care workers are expected to strive towards these values in all that they do. And they are expected to take an *ethical* approach, by having a clear sense of what is right and what is wrong.

Values lie at the heart of all care work and they are built into the health and social care National Occupational Standards. For example, a commitment to supporting care service users' rights is an important value – and these rights are set out in every NVQ unit:

> The rights that individuals have to:
>
> - be respected
> - be treated equally and not be discriminated against
> - be treated as an individual
> - be treated in a dignified way
> - privacy
> - be protected from danger and harm
> - be cared for in a way that meets their needs [and] takes account of their choices …
> - access information about themselves
> - communicate using their preferred methods of communication and language.
>
> (Skills for Care, 2005b, p. 3)

According to the National Occupational Standards, if you work in health and social care settings your key purpose is:

> … to provide an integrated, ethical and inclusive service, which meets agreed needs and outcomes of people requiring health and/or social care.
>
> (Skills for Care, 2005b, p. 2)

1.3 Principles of care practice

We have gone into detail in Section 1.2, to provide some background for the care skills work you will be doing throughout K101, so that you can see the framework within which care skills training and regulation are set. However, as a guide for working in practical situations you need something more manageable – a few key principles that you can hold in your head. For K101 we have pulled together, from the various standards and codes, five key principles of care practice.

The K101 principles of care practice

1   Support people in maximising their potential.
2   Support people in having a voice and being heard.
3   Respect people's beliefs and preferences.
4   Support people's rights to appropriate services.
5   Respect people's privacy and right to confidentiality.

The quotations in the five short sections below come from the National Occupational Standards for 'Health and Social Care' (Skills for Care, 2005a, 2005b, 2005c).

Support people in maximising their potential

This principle has links to such National Occupational Standards as:

> [You need to show that you] Develop supportive relationships that promote choice and independence [Section HSC35a]

> You need to show that you know, understand and can apply in practice … how to provide active support and place the preferences and best interest of individuals at the centre of everything you do, whilst enabling them to take responsibility (as far as they are able and within any restrictions placed upon them) and make and communicate their own decisions about their lives and actions to support their social, emotional and identity needs [Section HSC332, Knowledge Specification 2]

The National Occupational Standards definition of 'active support' is:

> Support that encourages individuals to do as much for themselves as possible to maintain their independence and physical ability and encourages people with disabilities to maximise their own potential and independence [Section HSC332].

Support people in having a voice and being heard

This links to such National Occupational Standards as:

> You need to show that … you support individuals to communicate their views and preferences regarding their current and future health and well-being needs and priorities [Section HSC35a, 2]

> You need to show that … you develop relationships in which individuals are able to express their fears, anxieties, feelings and concerns without worry of ridicule, rejection or retribution [Section HSC35c, 4].

Respect people's beliefs and preferences

> You need to show that … you treat and value each person as an individual and ensure that the support you give takes account of their needs and preferences [Section HSC35b, 2]

> You need to show that … you develop and maintain relationships that promote the views, preferences and independence of individuals and key people [Section HSC35a, 1]

> [You need to show that you] Respect the diversity and difference of individuals and key people [Section HSC35b]

> You need to show that … you work with individuals and key people in ways that provide support that is consistent with individuals' beliefs, culture, values and preferences [Section HSC35b, 3].

Key people here are:

> family; friends; carers; others with whom the individual has a supportive relationship [Section HSC35].

Support people's rights to appropriate services

> You need to show that … you work with individuals to identify the care and support:

- they can and wish to undertake themselves
- that can be provided through the individual's support networks
- that needs to be provided by yourself and others within and outside your organisation [Section HSC35a, 3].

Respect people's privacy and right to confidentiality

> You need to show that … you work with individuals in a way that respects their dignity, privacy and rights [Section HSC335b, 2].

As you can see, our K101 principles of care practice draw together a range of different specifications into a concise five-point manifesto.

1.4 Applying principles to practice

Now it is time to apply the five principles.

DVD

Activity 1   Observing care relationships in action

Allow about two hours

The rest of your work for this care skills element of Unit 4 is on the DVD. In the activities you find there you will be viewing examples of care practice and using the five principles to analyse and evaluate what you see.

Go to the DVD and find Block 1, Unit 4, Activity 1.

Comment

You have observed and analysed a variety of care situations, and you have seen how subtle the skills of maintaining good care relationships are. But also, by recording your observations and making recommendations, you have entered into the process of becoming sensitive to the requirements of care relationships and able to reflect on the consequences of different approaches.

Key points

- A care relationship is a special kind of relationship which needs to be set up and maintained with insight and skill.

- Good-quality care practice is promoted in the UK through National Occupational Standards, by codes of practice and by regulatory bodies.

- The important but rather overwhelming documentation produced by these bodies is boiled down, for the purposes of K101, to five key principles of care practice.

- By viewing examples of care practice and applying these five principles you have developed skills in:
  - observing and assessing care practice
  - identifying evidence of good and bad practice
  - recording what you observe
  - reflecting on your own practice.

- These skills will be particularly important if you are registered for the K101 Integrated Vocational Route (IVR).

2 Working with numbers

In Units 1, 2 and 3 you came across numbers here and there – a few percentages and an occasional pie chart. But sooner or later, in reading about health and social care, you will meet more complicated tables and charts than you have encountered so far. And you will need to be able to pull out relevant information from them.

Reader

Activity 2   Why numbers are important

Allow about 45 minutes

Number skills are considered to be important these days, whatever subject you study – but why? The first three sections of Chapter 8 of *The Good Study Guide* explain why. They also show that you are probably using many different kinds of number every day and almost certainly have some quite well-developed skills with numbers which you may not even have noticed.

Read Sections 8.1 to 8.3 of *The Good Study Guide* (pages 191–9).

Comment

I hope you are convinced that you are already quite numerate. So now you just need to develop the range of your skills.

Gaining confidence with tables and charts

Many tables and charts are not particularly difficult to read, they just take practice. It's like an unfamiliar dialect. At first you think that you can't understand, but then when you make the effort to attend carefully you realise that it all makes sense.

Of course, you may be quite confident and experienced in working with numbers, in which case the end-of-block activities will not take up much of your time. However, we know that many people who start out on health and social care studies do *not* feel confident about number work. If that includes you, then the number skills activities have been created especially for you.

The secret of making yourself more confident and skilled in reading tables and charts is to do it a little at a time. K101 does not aim to introduce you to any sophisticated statistics or complicated calculations. It just aims to focus on fairly simple tables and charts at the end of each block and explore what you can find out from them. You will be guided in this step by step through activities, so you should find it all quite straightforward. And by the end of the course we hope you will feel a lot more confident about making sense of numbers.

Activity 3   Is home care growing or declining?

Allow about 40 minutes

In this activity you follow up the discussion of home care in Unit 3 by looking at some figures showing how hours of home care have changed over time. This activity is on the DVD.

When you have completed the activity you will see that there is a link to a short assignment involving questions about the table you have just been working on. These are very similar to the exercises you will have just done. If you click on the link you can do the assignment straight away, while your memory of the table is still fresh. It won't take you long, so it isn't worth putting off.

Go to the DVD and find Block 1, Unit 4, Activity 3.

Comment

I hope you agree that reading the table was quite straightforward, and that you were also able to send off your number skills assignment without difficulty.

If you ran into a problem, you could try asking a question in the online forums. You may even find that someone has beaten you to it and there is already a discussion of how to get the assignment sent off. Otherwise, you could contact your tutor. It's important to get these things sorted out quickly and not let them put you off your stroke.

In any case, I hope you now feel reasonably confident about tackling the number skills exercise when you come to the end of Block 2.

3 Learning skills

This last part of Unit 4 takes up the important theme of developing the skills which will enable you to get the most from studying K101.

3.1 Reviewing your progress

You are approaching the end of the first K101 block. For four weeks you have been studying as an independent student, working from texts and the DVD, and with your online tutor group. How have you found it?

DVD

Activity 4   How are you feeling?

Allow about 15 minutes

This activity invites you to explore your thoughts about how well your K101 studies have gone so far. You will find a note sheet on the DVD to help with this.

Go to the DVD and find Block 1, Unit 4, Activity 4.

Comment

The process of reflection you have just been engaged in is one of the most important ways you can develop your learning skills. You are the best judge of what is working for you and what isn't. But when you are in the middle of things, it's easy to let yourself be swept along – not swimming to the bank but gradually going under. By making time to look around you and take stock, you allow yourself to draw on your large reserves of insight and resilience. And by writing things down, you get them out in the open, where you can see them and get them in proportion, instead of vaguely worrying about them.

You will be able to build on these reflections when you tackle TMA 02. You will see that there is a section where you are asked to write down a few thoughts on your progress so far.

Learning skills: Getting support from your tutor group

Why not visit your online tutor group forum and share your reflections? Find out whether others are having the same thoughts as you. It takes a lot of the strain out of studying if you can chat about how it's going. Studying is always challenging, but it puts things in perspective when you see that you are not alone in finding some things difficult. And to travel in company also increases the pleasure.

Independent study

There are many advantages of independent study of the kind you are doing with K101. You can move forward at your own pace, staying with a new idea until you have hold of it and are ready to move on. You can come back as often as you like, to check points again. You don't have to scribble sheaves of illegible lecture notes – you just write ideas onto the texts as you read. And because a course like this is tightly structured, you don't waste time and effort. You are given all the information you need, but only what you need. And the interlinking of texts, DVD and internet provides an unusually rich learning experience.

Learning skills: Getting the most from K101

This kind of course offers a lot, but it requires an active, positive approach on your part. A light skim through the texts won't work. You need to concentrate on what is said, think for yourself about questions that are asked, and have a proper go at activities. Have pen and paper handy, so that you can work with the thoughts and ideas that come to you as you study. And when you come to a key points box check that you really understand the points. Be prepared to go back and reread if you don't. Thinking back over your first four weeks of study, is this the approach you have taken – or do you need to make some adjustments for Block 2?

3.2 Working with the K101 learning outcomes

The K101 *learning outcomes* are a formal statement of what the course sets out to teach and what is expected of you in the course assessment. They are what a validation body, or an employer, might look at to arrive at a judgement of what K101 teaches.

The course learning outcomes are listed in the Course Guide. Normally, though, you will meet the outcomes, a few at a time, when you are working on your assignments. In the guidance for each assignment you are told which outcomes the assignment assesses, and your tutor will provide feedback on the progress you have made towards these outcomes.

Learning skills: Keeping the learning outcomes in proportion

The course learning outcomes play a useful role in highlighting the different kinds of learning you are doing as you study K101. However, the language of learning outcomes is inevitably quite general and formal, so it's not always easy to work with. It can make assignments look unnecessarily complicated, especially when there are lists of different outcomes. So it is important to keep learning outcomes in proportion.

- To a large extent, while you are working on an assignment, you can leave the learning outcomes in the background and concentrate on the specific questions you are asked. These questions, and the guidance that goes with them, usually give you quite enough to think about.

- It's when you are taking a broader look at your studies that the learning outcomes can be useful – in helping you to think about how well you are progressing across the whole range of learning, whether you are putting your energies into the right things, and whether you might need to seek extra support.

- And, of course, when you are applying for jobs, or planning future studies, the course learning outcomes help to remind you of all the learning you have achieved – what you can tell potential employers and what you can build on in further courses.

Learning outcomes for Block 1

Course learning outcomes come in four varieties (the same four varieties in every Open University course). Each K101 block and its accompanying assignment have learning outcomes under all four headings. We can look at the Block 1 learning outcomes to see how they work.

Knowledge and understanding

The knowledge and understanding learning outcome for Block 1 is this:

- After studying K101 you should be able to demonstrate knowledge and understanding of the scale and variety of caring activity within the UK, the complexity and sensitivity of individual care situations, and the main health care and social care services through which care and support are provided.

This might seem a bit overwhelming when you first read it, but if you stop to think you will soon see that it describes exactly what you have been learning about.

- **The scale and variety of caring activity within the UK.** In Unit 1 you learned about the enormous scale of family caring within the UK, and the variety of situations and needs covered; in Unit 2 you learned about the variety of health care services available in local communities and in hospitals, particularly in relation to diabetes; and in Unit 3 you learned about social care services, particularly home care services and different ways in which they are delivered and funded.

- **The complexity and sensitivity of individual care situations.** The very different case studies – for example, about Ann and Angus, Anwar, and the various clients of Somebody Cares – all focused attention on how complicated care situations can be, and how sensitively they need to be approached.

- **The main health care and social care services.** You learned about health care services in Unit 2 and about social care services in Unit 3.

So, you can see that this learning outcome is not a 'challenge' to you. It is simply a description of what you know and understand as a result of reading Block 1. And when you write your essay, you will be providing evidence that this is what you know and understand.

Cognitive skills

'Thinking skills' is another way of saying cognitive skills. As you study K101, you will gradually become more familiar with the disciplined kind of thinking that is the trademark of academic subjects. For K101 we have divided this into four aspects, and for the Block 1 assignment you focus on the first. (You can look in the Course Guide if you want to see the other three.)

- Describe care situations objectively, focusing on important points and leaving out unimportant details.

Reader

In ordinary life, when we talk with other people we tend to mix in our emotions and personal biases along with calmer judgements. But in university writing you are meant to try to leave out your personal feelings and just focus on accurate, useful description. (You can read more about objectivity on pages 88–9 of *The Good Study Guide*.) You are also meant to try to keep things brief and not take up time with irrelevant details. You will get more practised at this as you write assignments throughout K101, but we draw attention to this particular skill in the first assignment.

Key skills

University study teaches you about more than just an academic subject. It equips you with general skills which are useful in all walks of life, including employment. There are nationally specified key skills which university programmes are expected to teach. The key skills outcomes for Block 1 are:

- **Communicate ideas and arguments in a logical and well-structured way.** This learning outcome is the same for every assignment, but we give it a slightly different emphasis for each. As you work on your K101 essays and read the advice that goes with them, you will be addressing this outcome. In Block 1 the focus is on understanding what is meant by presenting 'an argument' in an essay and how to organise yourself to do so.

- **Read and interpret simple tables, charts and graphs.** This outcome is also the same for every assignment and is met by the work you do for the number skills part of this unit and the other end-of-block skills units. It is assessed when you send off your computer-marked assignment.

- **Confidently use a computer and the internet for basic learning activities.** You worked towards this outcome when you followed the guidance on how to log on to your OU StudentHome page and join your online tutor group forum, and when you learned how to submit TMA 01. This was assessed when you received credit for leaving messages in the appropriate sub-forum.

- **Manage your studies better, learn more effectively and do yourself justice in assessments.** This outcome is addressed when you read the learning skills boxes scattered through the K101 units, the learning skills sections in the end-of-block skills units, and *The Good Study Guide*. It is assessed through the brief reflective notes you are asked to write for your assignment.

Practice and/or professional skills

University study can also equip you with skills relevant to a specific profession, or area of practice. K101 develops skills relevant to practice in health and social care. These are addressed through the 'care skills' sections in the end-of-block skills units, each of which explores a different aspect of care skill. As you know from your work on this unit, the focus for this block is 'care relationships'. Part B of your assignment will assess what you learned. The learning outcome is:

- Identify aspects of care relationships which conform, or fail to conform, to principles of good care practice.

I hope you will agree that these are all perfectly sensible, straightforward outcomes, which match up very well with what you have actually learned in Block 1. The learning outcomes for the other blocks will take a very similar form, but we won't write about them in detail, as we have this time. Having seen how they work, we hope it will be fairly obvious how to make sense of them.

Key points

- Learning outcomes help you to recognise the many different kinds of learning you do as you study a course like K101.

- It is important to keep learning outcomes in proportion and not to let formal language and detail put you off. Use them when they are useful, but let them stay in the background until you need them.

- The K101 learning outcomes provide a formal description of what the course teaches and what is assessed. They are listed in the Course Guide and also appear in the Assessment Guide as they become relevant to particular assignments. You will be aware of them mainly in connection with assignments. You may also find them useful in letting people know what the course teaches.

3.3 Writing assignments

The course assignments are much more than an exercise at the end of a block to check what you have learned (although they do serve that purpose). The essays you write are likely to be the part of the course through which you learn most intensively.

Learning through writing

Writing essays brings the ideas and information you have been reading about in the course into clearer focus. You will find yourself pushed into sorting things out in your head in a way that makes some kind of sense to you. Even more important, by putting these thoughts into words you begin to make the new ideas your own – not just something you 'memorised' to pass a test, but knowledge you can use for your own purposes. At the same time, you will be learning to 'speak the language' of health and social care studies, so that gradually you find it easier to say what you want to.

At the end of a course, and often many years later, the essays you have written tend to be what you remember best. They make a lasting impression on your way of thinking about the world.

The challenge of writing

Because you learn so much through the writing, essays are challenging. If you find them difficult, don't worry that there's something wrong. Thinking hard and finding the right words for your thoughts is tough work, but it is also the essence of learning. So recognise essays for what they are: the core of your learning experience, challenging but essential.

Treat the essays with respect by building yourself up towards them. But don't go too far and let yourself get weighed down. Start your thinking early by looking at the assignment a week or two ahead. Expect the preparation and planning to take at least as long as the actual writing. Be sure to allow enough writing time to do yourself justice. And try to arrange things so that you don't have to write the whole essay in one go. The quality will improve a lot if you can come back and rework what you have written. Think of the essays as far more than a last-minute chore. Instead, treat them as a key learning opportunity, deserving of serious time and energy.

Finally, be sure to get assignments off to your tutor by the deadlines. Don't wait to get them perfect. Most people worry that they haven't done very well at the moment of finishing an assignment. You just have to do the best you can in the time available. Then let it go. You may find that you have done better than you think. But in any case it is important to be able to put each essay behind you and move on to the next block of work. You could spend forever worrying about it otherwise.

You will be given lots of advice on how to tackle essays, in the Assessment Guide and *The Good Study Guide*. Better still, your tutor will try to help you with essay writing as much as with your understanding of the course. One of the major objectives of K101 is that you should consider yourself a much better essay writer by the end, regardless of how skilled you may or may not feel now. Looking back, you may feel that the writing side was the part of the course from which you gained most.

Activity 5   Finding out what a good essay is

Allow about an hour and a half

Reader

You will be writing a K101 essay about every four weeks. But are you clear what you are aiming for in your essays? Your tutor's comments on your Unit 1 essay will give you some insight. But you can get a lot more ideas from *The Good Study Guide*.

Read the first three sections of Chapter 10 of *The Good Study Guide* (pages 245–62) and do the activities. By the end, you will have more idea of what your tutor is looking for in marking your essay.

It's a good idea to follow the recommendation at the top of page 250 to download copies of the short sample essays from the Good Study Guide website www.goodstudyguide.co.uk. This will make the activities easier.

Comment

It may have seemed quite a difficult choice to invest time in looking at other people's essays, when you had one of your own to write. However, I hope you feel that thinking about where other people get it right or wrong has put you in a better position to tackle your own essay.

End-of-block assignment

You have now almost completed Block 1. Your last task is assignment TMA 02. You will find details in the Assessment Guide.

References

General Social Care Council (2002) *Code of Practice for Social Care Workers and Code of Practice for Employers of Social Care Workers*, London, General Social Care Council; also available online at: www.gscc.org.uk (Accessed 3 February 2008).

Skills for Care (2005a) HSC335 *Contribute to the Protection of Individuals from Harm and Abuse*, National Occupational Standards Health and Social Care [online], www.topssengland.net/view.asp?id=57 (Accessed 3 February 2008).

Skills for Care (2005b) HSC35 *Promote Choice, Well-being and the Protection of All Individuals*, National Occupational Standards Health and Social Care [online], www.topssengland.net/view.asp?id=57 (Accessed 3 February 2008).

Skills for Care (2005c) HSC332 *Support the Social, Emotional and Identity Needs of Individuals*, National Occupational Standards Health and Social Care [online], www.topssengland.net/view.asp?id=57 (Accessed 3 February 2008).

Skills for Care (undated) *Who We Are and What We Do* [online], www.topssengland.net/ (Accessed 4 March 2008).

Websites

www.ccwales.org.uk/ (Accessed 26 February 2008).

www.goodstudyguide.co.uk/ (Accessed 26 February 2008).

www.niscc.info/ (Accessed 26 February 2008).

www.skillsforhealth.org.uk/ (Accessed 26 February 2008).

www.sqa.org.uk/ (Accessed 26 February 2008).

www.sssc.uk.com/Homepage.htm (Accessed 26 February 2008).

www.topssengland.net (Accessed 26 February 2008).

Course team

Production team

Andrew Northedge (Chair)

Joanna Bornat (Deputy Chair)

Corinne De Souza (Course Manager)

Maureen Richards (Course Manager)

Sarah Shelley (Course Team Assistant)

Dorothy Atkinson

Fiona Barnes

Ken Blakemore

Hilary Brown

Joyce Cavaye

Anne Fletcher

Marion Hall

Julia Johnson

Rebecca Jones

Ann Martin

Mo McPhail

Ingrid Nix

Sheila Peace

Mary Twomey

Jan Walmsley

Naomi Watson

Fran Wiles

Media production team

Phil Greaney, Fiona Harris, Matthew Moran, Jenny Nockles (Editorial Media Developers); Paul Bishop, Ray Guo (Interactive Media Developers); Vicky Eves (Graphic Artist); Debbie Crouch (Designer); Judy Thomas (Librarian); Adrian Bickers, Michelle Woolley (Media Project Managers); Philippa Broadbent, Ann Carter, Kim Dulson, Siggy Martin (Print Buyers); Sas Amoah, Bisiola Arogundade (Media Assistants); Martin Chiverton (Executive Sound and Vision Producer); Carole Brown (Sound and Vision Assistant); Gail Block, Melisa Ekdoghan, Phil Gauron, Annie Morgan (Clear Focus Productions); Lindsay Brigham, Phil Coleman (Integrated Vocational Route); Richard Norris, Harry Venning (Cartoonists).

External assessor

Jon Glasby, University of Birmingham

Critical readers

John Adams, James Blewett, Ian Buchanan, Barry Cooper, Celia Davies, Monica Dowling, Sarah Earle, Ric Estee-Wale, Elizabeth Forbat, Sandy Fraser, Sally French, Teresa Geraghty, Leonie Kellaher, Aine MacNamara, Mick McCormick, Paul McDonald, Ann Mitchell, Alun Morgan, Janet Seden, Sam Parboteah, Vijay Patel, Jenny Pearce, Lucy Rai, Martin Robb, Angela Russell, Patricia Taylor, Linda Walker.

Developmental testers

John Dow, Tamsin Dunsdon, Trisha Shaw, Susan Underwood, Mark Vine.

Acknowledgements

Grateful acknowledgement is made to the following sources for permission to reproduce material in this book.

Text

© Community care; Common health questions, What are Primary Care Trusts (PCTs)?, NHS Direct, www.nhsdirect.nhs.uk. Crown copyright material is reproduced under Class Licence Number C01W0000065 with the permission of the Controller of HMSO and the Queen's Printer for Scotland; Hanbury, A. (2006) 'I look forward to getting my 70-year medal – I might even refuse a cure', Diabetes UK. Reproduced by permission; Common health questions, What services do hospitals provide? www.nhsdirect.nhs.uk Crown copyright material is reproduced under Class Licence Number C01W0000065 with the permission of the Controller of HMSO and the Queen's printer for Scotland; www.parliament. uk. Parliamentary Copyright Material is reproduced under licence number P2005000031, with the permission of the Controller of HMSO on behalf of Parliament; Heng, S. (2005) 'The Simon Heng Column', *Community Care*, 24 November 2005. Published by permission of the editor of Community Care.

Tables/illustrations/cartoons/other

Page 11: © www.johnbirdsall.co.uk; page 14: © Janine Wiedel Photolibrary/ Alamy, © www.johnbirdsall.co.uk, © Andy Sacks/Getty Images; page 22: © Ryan Pierse/Getty Images; page 27: © Kevin Horan/Getty Images, © Creative/Getty Images; page 31: © Two women sitting together laughing, www.parkinsons.org.uk/anout_us/what_we_do.aspx (Accessed 20 Sep 2007); page 65: © Barbara Peacock/Getty Images; page 67: © BananaStock/ Punchstock; page 73: © Peter Titmuss/Alamy; page 74: © Sally and Richard Greenhill/Alamy; page 82: © www.nhslotian.scot.nhs.uk, Lothian NHS Board; page 101: Andria Hanbury, Andie on Holiday [online] www.diabetes.org.uk; page 86@ © GARO/Phanie/Rex Features; page 90: © Vince Bevan/Alamy; page 92: © David Joel/Getty Images; page 95: © 67photo/Alamy; page 97: © workbook stock/Jupiter Images; page 98: © workbook stock/Jupiter Images; page 103: © Thomas Annan/Getty Images; page 122: CarenapE (Care Needs Assessment Package For The Elderly)(Version 3, August 1999), Crown copyright material is reproduced under Class Licence Number C01W0000065 with the permission of the Controller of HMSO and the Queen's Printer for Scotland; page 123: www.johnbirdsall.co.uk; page 124: adapted from Maslow A. H. (1970), *Motivation and Personality*, 3rd edn, Persona Education Inc.; page 127: www.johnbirdsall.co.uk; page 138: © John Chillingworth, Hulten Archive/ Getty Images.